AutoCAD LT® 2000i

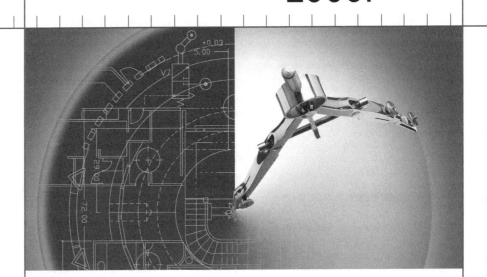

GETTING STARTED

05720-017400-5001   June 2000

Autodesk Trademarks

Third Party Trademarks

Third Party Software Program Credits

GOVERNMENT USE

Contents

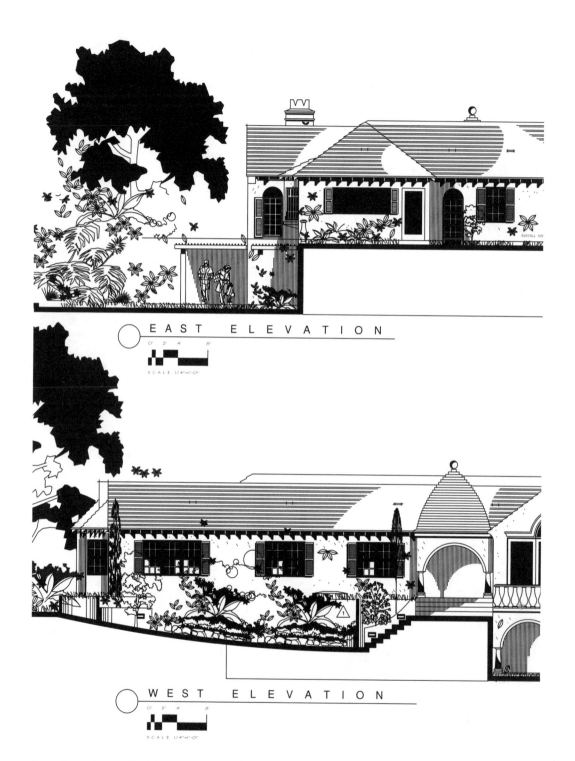

EAST ELEVATION

0' 2' 4' 8'

SCALE 1/4"=1'-0"

WEST ELEVATION

0' 2' 4' 8'

SCALE 1/4"=1'-0"

Drawing created with AutoCAD LT® 2000i

Introducing
AutoCAD LT

AutoCAD LT® is software that automates the process of producing precision drawings for engineers, architects, landscape designers, and others. Computer-aided design (CAD) tools such as AutoCAD LT streamline the design of objects from bolts to bridges by making it simple to create and change drawings before committing them to paper. Although the principles of creating precision drawings have not changed, Autodesk® has revolutionized the tools.

In this chapter

- What Is AutoCAD LT?
- What's New in AutoCAD LT 2000i?
- Getting Information About AutoCAD LT
- Using Active Assistance

What Is AutoCAD LT?

AutoCAD LT 2000i is easy-to-use two-dimensional (2D) design and drafting software. It provides software tools that replace the traditional drafting board, pencil, pen, triangle, and T-square. AutoCAD LT is the ideal solution for people who are new to CAD and for professionals who require occasional CAD use in extended design teams.

The leading low-cost professional 2D CAD software, AutoCAD LT delivers AutoCAD® compatibility and substantial drafting productivity.

Drafting Productivity

Using the intuitive AutoCAD LT tools helps you work efficiently. You can reuse elements from electronic drawings easily, which cuts down the time you spend reworking similar designs. And you can share electronic drawings over a local area network—even the World Wide Web.

The AutoCAD LT tools described in this book give you

- Higher productivity
- Greater drawing accuracy and consistency
- More time to design creatively

AutoCAD Compatibility

AutoCAD LT 2000i is the only 2D CAD software that provides 100% AutoCAD 2000i drawing compatibility. Although AutoCAD software can create and edit some objects that cannot be created in AutoCAD LT, the programs share the same Autodesk drawing file format (DWG).

As an AutoCAD LT user, you can have complete confidence when opening AutoCAD drawings because

- AutoCAD LT reads and displays objects created in AutoCAD
- No data is lost when you edit a file in AutoCAD LT and then reopen it in AutoCAD

The interfaces of AutoCAD and AutoCAD LT are almost identical. So, AutoCAD LT is the perfect solution for managers, supervisors, and other technical professionals who need to view and edit AutoCAD drawings with absolute accuracy. And those users who need to take their drawings into the field on a laptop computer can do so easily with AutoCAD LT.

Differences Between AutoCAD LT and AutoCAD

AutoCAD LT 2000i shares many features with AutoCAD 2000i. The products overlap for most 2D tasks. However, a few important differences distinguish the two programs. Because AutoCAD LT is basically a 2D product with limited customization capabilities, it does not offer

- Advanced 3D design, visualization, and raster capabilities
- Support for Visual Basic or AutoLISP® customization
- Support for customized applications designed for use with AutoCAD

For more specific information about the differences between the two products, see page 228.

What's New in AutoCAD LT 2000i?

New features in AutoCAD LT 2000i work to make you more productive.

Leveraging the Internet

Two new communication and collaboration tools leverage the Internet to make up-to-date information available to team members and clients.

- *AutoCAD LT Today.* Use the Today window as a content-rich portal to the Internet. Displaying an intranet-based bulletin board in the Today window can provide project information, standards, software patches, and shared files deployed by your organization. Adding and personalizing the Autodesk Web site for design industry resources, called Autodesk Point A, can integrate access to industry news, tools, and tips with AutoCAD LT.
- *Publish to Web.* Walk through the creation and editing of Web pages that include drawing images using the Publish to Web wizard. The wizard helps you select a template, add images, specify a Web server, and publish your page to that location without the services of an Internet professional. The predesigned page formats include DWF and JPG images.

Facilitating Design Sharing with Meet Now

The Meet Now feature uses Microsoft NetMeeting technology for hosting meetings on the Internet and intranets. You can use Meet Now to automatically start NetMeeting from inside AutoCAD LT, establish a meeting, and share a drawing session with participants. When one workstation completes a command, another participant is free to interact with the shared drawing.

Meet Now is an excellent teaching and communication tool. It can be used for educating colleagues about new features, verifying designs online, and explaining design changes to designers no matter where they are located.

Using Improved File Navigation

The Today window includes these file navigation tabs:

- *Open Drawings.* Easily locate and open recently used drawing files.
- *Create Drawings.* Start with a template, use a drawing setup wizard, or start from scratch.
- *Symbol Libraries.* Find needed information consolidated in one location.

The redesigned standard file selection dialog boxes facilitate quick access to commonly used files and file locations. The places list on the left side of the dialog boxes provides handy access to always available *History*, *Personal*, and *Favorites* folders as well as the RedSpark and Buzzsaw.com Web sites. In addition, you can browse FTP sites for files using these new dialog boxes.

Streamlining Layer Management by Saving Settings

Saving layer settings is the equivalent of taking a snapshot of current layer properties and states. After naming each group of settings you save, you can then quickly restore them. For example, you might want to restore one group of settings for editing, use another group for printing on a system printer, and have an additional group available for use with a pen plotter. You can export saved layer setting files and easily import them into other drawings.

Learning Quickly with Active Assistance

Active Assistance is a new feature that can help you learn to use AutoCAD LT. As you work, the Active Assistance window automatically displays context-sensitive information regarding the task at hand. For example, when you begin drawing a polygon, Active Assistance displays information about the three different ways you can accomplish the task. If you need details, such as step-by-step procedures, you can click links in Active Assistance that open related topics in online Help. For more information about using Active Assistance, see page 8.

Getting Information About AutoCAD LT

This *Getting Started* guide provides an overview of the most commonly used features of AutoCAD LT. New users should use it to familiarize themselves with AutoCAD LT so they can begin working quickly. Additional resources are available when more information is needed.

- *Online Help* provides in-depth procedures, conceptual information, and command descriptions.
- *Learning Assistance* provides a series of online tutorial lessons.
- *What's New* provides a brief online tour of new features.

Accessing Online Help

Keyword references appear at the end of most *Getting Started* topics:

ONLINE HELP   MODEL, LAYOUT

Search for the LAYOUT keyword on the Help system Index tab to find and view related concepts, procedures, commands, and system variables.

Click to display concepts related to selected topic.

Click to display procedures related to selected topic.

Click to display command information related to selected topic.

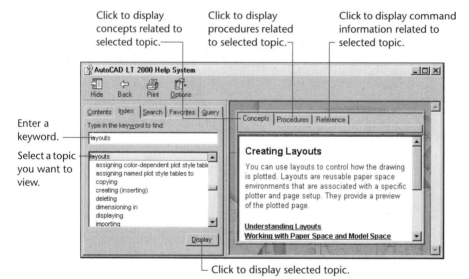

Enter a keyword.

Select a topic you want to view.

Click to display selected topic.

You can also perform a *natural language query* by clicking the Query tab and entering a question. For example, you could enter

How do I create a layout?

For specific instructions about using online Help, find the *Using the AutoCAD LT Help System* topic in the AutoCAD LT Help system.

Using AutoCAD LT Learning Assistance

AutoCAD LT Learning Assistance™ is an interactive tool that includes short animations. *Concept* animations give you an overview of some of the general terms you need to know to use AutoCAD LT. *Tutorial lessons* walk you through step-by-step procedures.

Learning Assistance includes an orientation with instructions for its use.

NOTE The AutoCAD LT Quick Reference card provides an easy-to-use graphical key to the AutoCAD LT interface, toolbars, shortcut keys, system variables, command aliases, and basic operations such as selecting objects.

To get started	
Action	**Menu**
Accessing online Help	Help ➤ AutoCAD LT Help Topics
Using Learning Assistance	Help ➤ Learning Assistance
Viewing What's New	Help ➤ What's New

Using Active Assistance

The Active Assistance window provides handy nuggets of information that change dynamically as you work. Often the guidance you get from Active Assistance is just enough to get you started performing unfamiliar or rarely used tasks.

Linking to Additional Information

To get additional information, click links in the Active Assistance window. Clicking a link expands the current Active Assistance topic.

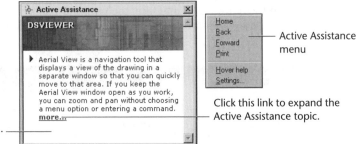

Right-click in the Active Assistance window to display a shortcut menu.

Active Assistance menu

Click this link to expand the Active Assistance topic.

Navigating the Active Assistance Topics

You can right-click in the Active Assistance window to display a shortcut menu with navigation commands. Use these commands to move forward and backward or return to Home in the Active Assistance window, as you would in a Web browser.

Controlling Active Assistance Settings

Active Assistance is displayed, by default, in the upper-right corner of the AutoCAD LT 2000i window. You can use an option in the Active Assistance Settings dialog box to choose not to display Active Assistance automatically when AutoCAD LT 2000i starts. Alternatively, you can select one of these options in the Active Assistance Settings dialog box to automatically start Active Assistance

- Every time you start a command
- Only when you start a command that is new or enhanced in AutoCAD LT 2000i
- Only when dialog boxes are displayed
- Only when you double-click the Active Assistance icon

NOTE At times, you might want to manually close the Active Assistance window. Double-clicking the Assist icon in the system tray, which is usually located in the lower-right corner of your screen, reopens the window. To turn off Active Assistance, right-click the Assist icon and choose Exit.

┌─Assist icon

An additional option in the Active Assistance Settings dialog box turns on Hover Help, which changes Active Assistance for dialog boxes. Select this option if you want the Active Assistance window to display details about individual dialog box features when you hold your cursor over them. Clear it if you want Active Assistance to display help for the entire dialog box.

To get started		
Action	**Menu**	**Toolbar**
Using Active Assistance	Help ➤ Active Assistance	Standard
Printing Active Assistance Topics	Right-click for shortcut menu	
Controlling Active Assistance Settings	Right-click for shortcut menu	

ONLINE HELP ASSIST

Using CAD and a network, you and offsite team members can work on a single drawing. As you make changes, they appear on your colleagues' screens. Then someone else's editing appears on your screen.

Before the rise of the Internet, you had to collaborate with others by meeting face-to-face or using phone, fax, courier, or mail.

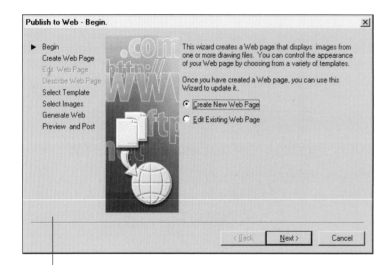

Computer-aided design (CAD) takes full advantage of the Internet. Now you can share drawings by publishing them to a Web site. The example shows results of a test administered at a remote location.

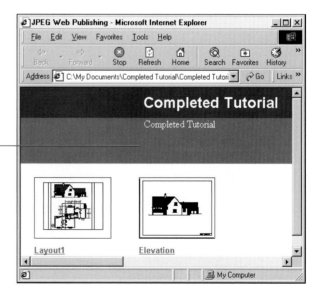

Making the Transition from Paper to CAD

1

If you are new to computer-aided design (CAD), congratulations.

Switching from manual drafting to AutoCAD LT® can make you more productive. Using drafting terms you're already familiar with, this chapter introduces equivalent CAD concepts. Drawings from AutoCAD LT customers illustrate each topic.

CAD concepts are explained more fully in later chapters. You can also look up the words shown in italics in the online Help index to find more information.

In this chapter

- Drawing to Scale
- Laying Out Your Drawing
- Organizing Drawing Information
- Establishing Drafting Standards
- Drawing Efficiently
- Drawing Accurately
- Viewing Your Drawing
- Creating Standard Symbols
- Creating Dimensions and Text
- Modifying Your Drawing
- Incorporating Other Drawings

Drawing to Scale

Drawing scale is something you consider when laying out your drawing. You establish scale differently in CAD than you do with manual drafting.

With manual drafting, you must determine the scale of a view before you start drawing. This scale compares the size of the actual object to the size of the model drawn on paper.

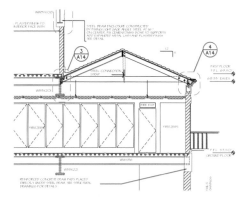

Draw the object at full scale in the units you specify.

In AutoCAD LT, you define the type of unit you will use, and then draw your design without regard to scale. You consider scaling later, when you lay out and plot your drawing.

To start, set the *unit of measurement* you will use for your model: feet and inches, meters, kilometers, and so on. For example, when you draw a motor part, one unit might equal one millimeter. When you draw a map, one unit might equal one kilometer.

This drawing of a foundation plan uses the setting for feet and inches. Views of the building were scaled to create the layout for the printed drawing, using one scale for the details and another for the building itself.

Chapter 5, "Drawing Setup" and Chapter 14, "Creating Layouts and Plotting"

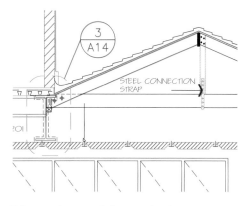

When you lay out and plot your drawing, you can set any scale you like.

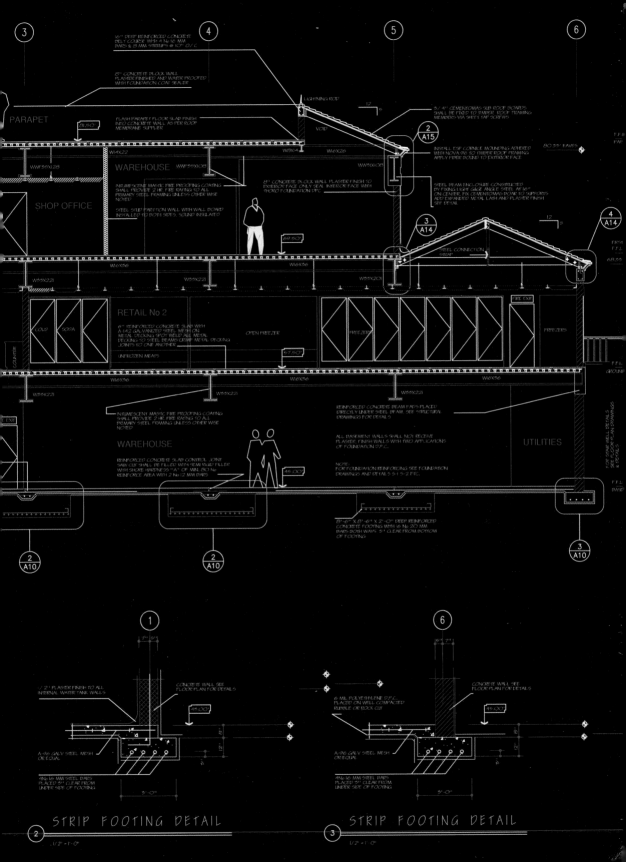

③ ④ ⑤ ⑥

16" DEEP REINFORCED CONCRETE
BELT COURSE WITH 4 No 16 MM
BARS & 8 MM STIRRUPS @ 10" O/C

8" CONCRETE BLOCK WALL
PLASTER FINISHED AND WATER PROOFED
WITH FOUNDATION COAT SEALER

LIGHTNING ROD

12 : 6

3/4" CEMENTOMAS SUB ROOF BOARDS
SHALL BE FIXED TO TIMBER ROOF FRAMING
MEMBERS VIA SHEET TAP SCREWS

PARAPET

VOID

② A15

80 33' EAVES

F.F.L.
PAR

FLASH PARAPET FLOOR SLAB FINISH
INTO CONCRETE WALL AS PER ROOF
MEMBRANE SUPPLIER

81.50'

INSTALL ESF CORNICE MOUNDING ADHERED
WITH NOVA 96 TO TIMBER ROOF FRAMING
APPLY FIBER BOUND TO EXTERIOR FACE

WAREHOUSE

W6X22 W6X4 W6X26 WW5IX109

WWF56X128 WWF56X109

SHOP OFFICE

INTUMESCENT MASTIC FIRE PROOFING COATING
SHALL PROVIDE 2 HR FIRE RATING TO ALL
PRIMARY STEEL FRAMING UNLESS OTHER WISE
NOTED

STEEL STUD PARTITION WALL WITH WALL BOARD
INSTALLED TO BOTH SIDES, SOUND INSULATED

69.50'

8" CONCRETE BLOCK WALL PLASTER FINISH TO
EXTERIOR FACE ONLY. SEAL INTERIOR FACE WITH
THORO FOUNDATION DPC

STEEL BEAM ENCLOSURE CONSTRUCTED
BY FIXING LIGHT GAGE ANGLE STEEL AT 16"
ON CENTER, FIX CEMENTOMAS BOARD TO SUPPORTS
ADD EXPANDED METAL LATH AND PLASTER FINISH
SEE DETAIL

③ A14

12 : 8

④ A14

STEEL CONNECTION
STRAP

FINAL
F.F.L.
68.55'

W14X56 W16X56 W16X56 W55X201

RETAIL No 2

6" REINFORCED CONCRETE SLAB WITH
A 142 GALVANIZED STEEL MESH ON
METAL DECKING SPOT WELD ALL METAL
DECKING TO STEEL BEAMS CRIMP METAL DECKING
JOINTS TO ONE ANOTHER

COLD
SODA

OPEN FREEZER

PREEZER

FIRE EXIT

PREEZERS

UNFROZEN MEATS

97.50'

COUNTER

F.F.L.
GROUND

W16X56 W55X221 W16X56 W6X221

W55X221 W55X221

INTUMESCENT MASTIC FIRE PROOFING COATING
SHALL PROVIDE 2 HR FIRE RATING TO ALL
PRIMARY STEEL FRAMING UNLESS OTHER WISE
NOTED

REINFORCED CONCRETE BEAM PADS PLACED
DIRECTLY UNDER STEEL BEAM, SEE STRUCTURAL
DRAWINGS FOR DETAILS

WAREHOUSE

ALL BASEMENT WALLS SHALL NOT RECEIVE
PLASTER, FINISH WALLS WITH TWO APPLICATIONS
OF FOUNDATION D.P.C.

UTILITIES

EXIT

REINFORCED CONCRETE SLAB CONTROL JOINT
SAW CUT SHALL BE FILLED WITH SEMI RIGID FILLER
WITH SHORE HARDNESS "A" OF MIN, BO No
REINFORCE AREA WITH 2 No 12 MM BARS

48.00'

NOTE:
FOR FOUNDATION REINFORCING SEE FOUNDATION
DRAWINGS AND DETAILS S-1 S-2 ETC.

F.F.L.
BASE

8'-6" X 8'-6" X 2'-0" DEEP REINFORCED
CONCRETE FOOTING WITH 16 No 20 MM
BARS BOTH WAYS 5" CLEAR FROM BOTTOM
OF FOOTING

③ A10

② A10 ② A10

① ⑥

1/2" PLASTER FINISH TO ALL
INTERNAL WATER TANK WALLS

CONCRETE WALL SEE
FLOOR PLAN FOR DETAILS

CONCRETE WALL SEE
FLOOR PLAN FOR DETAILS

48.00'

6 MIL POLYETHYLENE D.P.C.
PLACED ON WELL COMPACTED
RUBBLE OR ROCK CUT

48.00'

A-96 GALV STEEL MESH
OR EQUAL

A-96 GALV STEEL MESH
OR EQUAL

4No 16 MM STEEL BARS
PLACED 5" CLEAR FROM
UNDER SIDE OF FOOTING

4No 16 MM STEEL BARS
PLACED 5" CLEAR FROM
UNDER SIDE OF FOOTING

5'-0" 5'-0"

STRIP FOOTING DETAIL

STRIP FOOTING DETAIL

② 1/2"=1'-0" ③ 1/2"=1'-0"

Laying Out Your Drawing

The drawing layout is fundamental to a well-designed drawing. On paper, a layout is constrained by the sheet size you use. In CAD, you are not limited to one particular layout or sheet size.

When you draft manually, you first select a sheet, which usually includes a preprinted border and title block. Then you determine the location for views—plans, elevations, sections, and details. Finally, you start to draw.

You create your basic design, or model, in a drawing area known as model space.

With AutoCAD LT, you first draw your design, or model, in a working environment called *model space*. You can then create several layouts for that model in an environment called *paper space*.

Each layout represents a different drawing sheet. It typically contains a border, title block, general notes, and several views of the model arranged in layout *viewports*. Viewports are areas, similar to windows, through which you can see your model. You scale the views in viewports by *zooming* in or out.

In this drawing of a cottage, layout viewports display the model in plan and elevation views.

Chapter 5, "Drawing Setup" and Chapter 14, "Creating Layouts and Plotting"

When you're ready to print, you can arrange different views of your model in a layout.

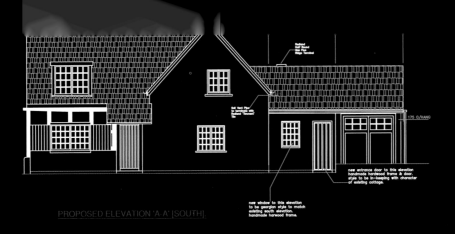

Redland Half Round Gas Flue Ridge Terminal

Soil Vent Pipe to terminate with Redland "Renown" Tile

1175 O/HANG

new entrance door to this elevation handmade hardwood frame & door. style to be in-keeping with character of existing cottage.

new window to this elevation to be georgian style to match existing south elevation. handmade harwood frame.

PROPOSED ELEVATION 'A-A' [SOUTH].

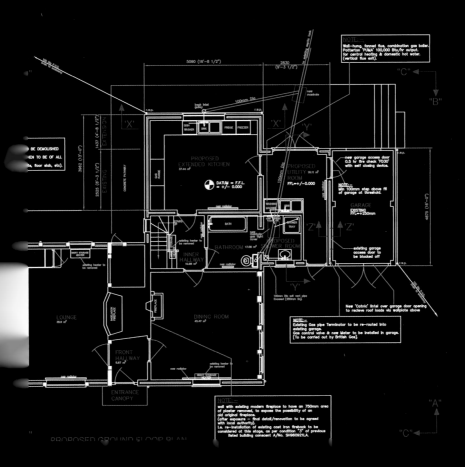

5090 (16'-8 1/2")   2630 (8'-3 1/2")

NOTE:—
Wall-hung, fanned flue, combination gas boiler. Potterton 'PUMA' 100,000 Btu/hr output. for central heating & domestic hot water. (vertical flue exit).

"C"
"B"
"C"

1437 (4'-8 1/2")   EXTENSION

3962 (13'-0")   EXISTING

2525 (8'-3 1/2")

'X'   'X'   "Y"

BE DEMOLISHED
HEN TO BE OF ALL.
tile, floor slab, etc).

CONCRETE PATHWAY

100mm Dia

new manhole

bosh inlet gulley

DISH WASHER   FRIDGE FREEZER

PROPOSED EXTENDED KITCHEN
37.44 m²

DATUM = F.F.L.
= +/- 0.000

PROPOSED UTILITY ROOM   16.11 m²
FFL=+/-0.000

new garage access door 0.5 hr fire check 'FD30' with self closing device.

NOTE:—
Min 100mm step above fll of garage at threshold.

GARAGE
EXISTING
FFL=+250mm

BATH

'Z'   'Z'

existing heater to be removed

INNER HALLWAY
10.68 m²

BATHROOM   17.06 m²

PROPOSED SHOWER ROOM

existing garage access door to be blocked off

LOUNGE
35.9 m²

INGLENOOK FIREPLACE

FIREPLACE

DINING ROOM
43.47 m²

'Y'

100mm Dia soil vent pipe Encased [250mm Sq].

New 'Catnic' lintel over garage door opening to recieve roof loads via wallplate above

NOTE:—
Existing Gas pipe Terminator to be re-routed into existing garage.
Gas control valve & new Meter to be installed in garage. [To be carried out by British Gas].

FRONT HALLWAY
5.67 m²

new radiator

existing heater to be removed

ENTRANCE CANOPY

NOTE:—
wall with existing modern fireplace to have an 750mm area of plaster removed, to expose the possibility of an old original fireplace.
(after exposure — final detail/renovation to be agreed with local authority).
i.e. re-installation of existing cast iron fireback to be considered at this stage, as per condition "J" of previous listed building consent A/No. SH960921LA.

"A"

"C"

PROPOSED GROUND FLOOR PLAN

1
2
3
4

Organizing Drawing Information

In both manual drafting and CAD, you need a way to organize your drawing content—a method for separating, sorting, and editing specific drawing data.

With manual drafting, you can separate information onto individual transparent overlays. For example, a building plan might contain separate overlays for its structural, electrical, and plumbing components.

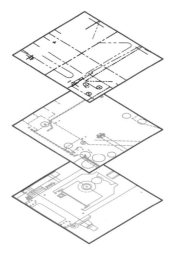

Turn off layers to hide complex details as you work.

In AutoCAD LT, *layers* are equivalent to transparent overlays. As with overlays, you can display, edit, and print layers separately or in combination.

You can name layers to help track content, and lock layers so they can't be altered. Assigning settings such as color, *linetype,* or *lineweight* to layers helps you comply with industry standards.

You can also use layers to organize drawing objects for plotting. Assigning a *plot style* to a layer makes all the objects drawn on that layer plot in a similar manner.

If you need to save time, you can change numerous layer settings at once. For example, you can save settings used for plotting and quickly restore them when needed.

This mechanical drawing of a press uses layers to define different linetypes and colors.

Display layers when you need to see all components.

Chapter 5, "Drawing Setup" and Chapter 9, "Making Modifications"

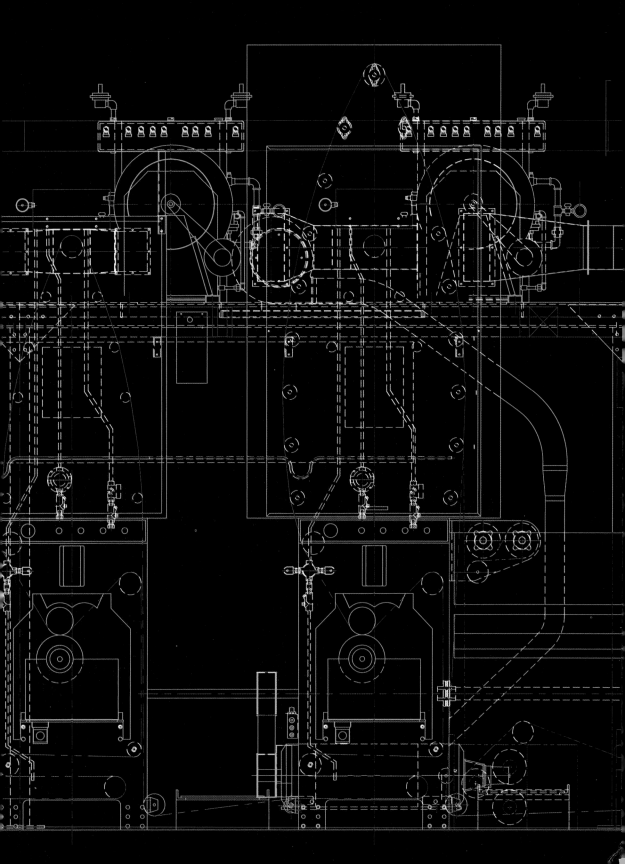

Establishing Drafting Standards

Whether you work as a member of a team or on an individual project, developing standards is a requirement for efficient communication.

 Manual drafting requires meticulous accuracy in drawing linetypes, lineweights, text, dimensions, and more. Standards must be established in the beginning and applied consistently.

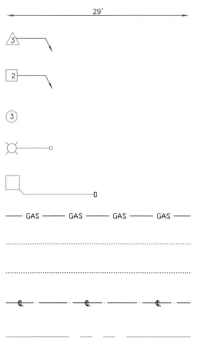

Dimension, text, and linetype styles can be established in a template drawing and used for creating new drawings.

 With AutoCAD LT, you can ensure conformity to industry or company standards by creating reusable styles that you can apply consistently.

You can create styles for text, dimensions, and linetypes. A text style, for example, establishes font and typeface characteristics such as height, width, and slant.

You can save styles, standard layers, viewport configurations, title block and border information, and some command settings in template drawings. Using *template drawings* helps you quickly start new drawings that conform to standards.

This drawing of a roadway plan uses styles to maintain drafting standards for text, dimensioning, and linetypes.

 Chapter 5, "Drawing Setup"

LENA ROAD

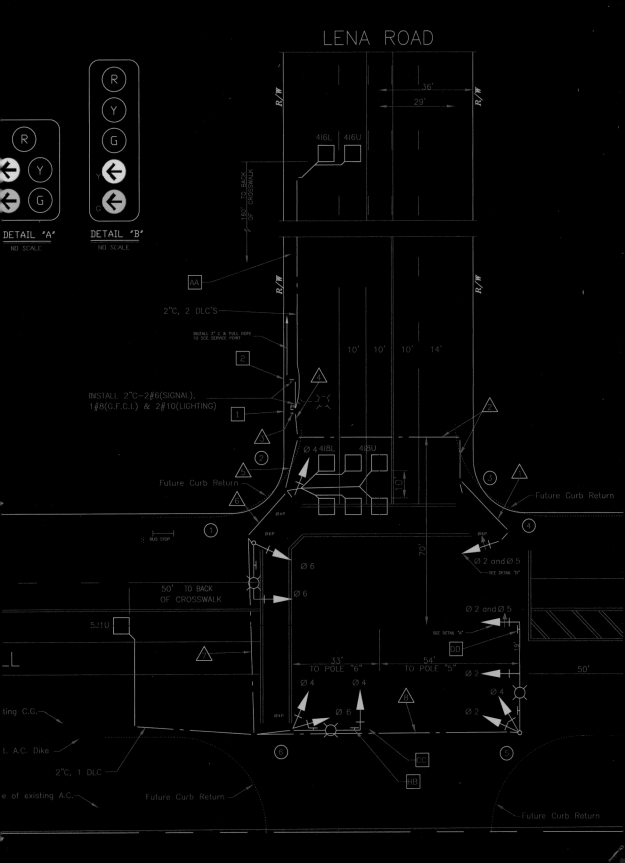

DETAIL "A"
NO SCALE

DETAIL "B"
NO SCALE

R/W

R/W

36'

29'

416L 416U

160' TO BACK OF CROSSWALK

R/W

R/W

AA

2"C, 2 DLC'S

INSTALL 3" C & PULL ROPE
TO SCE SERVICE POINT

10' 10' 10' 14'

2

4

INSTALL 2"C-2#6(SIGNAL),
1#8(G.F.C.I.) & 2#10(LIGHTING)

1

3

Ø 4 418L   418U

3

2

10'

5

Future Curb Return

3

1

6

Future Curb Return

Ø4P

1

4

BUS STOP

Ø6P

Ø6P

Ø 6

Ø 2 and Ø 5

SEE DETAIL "B"

50' TO BACK
OF CROSSWALK

Ø 6

70'

Ø 2 and Ø 5

SEE DETAIL "A"

5J1U

DD

Ø 2

7

33'
TO POLE "6"

54'
TO POLE "5"

19'

50'

ting C.G.

Ø 4   Ø 4

Ø 4

t. A.C. Dike

Ø4P

Ø 6

8

Ø 2

2"C, 1 DLC

e of existing A.C.

6

CC

5

Future Curb Return

BB

Future Curb Return

Drawing Efficiently

Draw with less effort and revise with more speed: these are the two main reasons you use CAD. AutoCAD LT has a complete set of drawing and editing tools to help eliminate repetitive, time-consuming drafting tasks.

 If you work with paper and a drawing board, your set of drawing tools is likely to include pencils, scales, parallel rules, templates, and erasers. Repetitive drawing and editing tasks must be done manually.

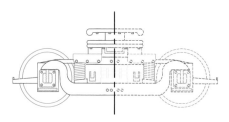

You can save drafting time by drawing one half of an item and then mirroring it to create the other half.

 In AutoCAD LT, the *graphics area* is your "paper" and your mouse replaces your pencil. You can choose from a variety of drawing tools that create lines, rectangles, circles, curves, and more.

With AutoCAD LT, you not only copy objects, you can scale, rotate, and mirror. You can move or copy objects between open drawings or within the same drawing. Editing is easy with stretch, align, and offset. To add hatching, simply drag a hatch pattern into the area to be filled.

In this drawing of a trolley, copying and mirroring were used to create repeated and symmetrical features. Offsetting lines and hatching were also used to draw more efficiently.

 Chapter 8, "Drawing Objects" and Chapter 9, "Making Modifications"

Drawing Accurately

Engineering and architectural drawing require a high degree of accuracy. With CAD you draft more accurately than with manual methods.

 On paper, you must draw objects carefully to ensure correct size and alignment. Objects drawn to scale must be manually verified and dimensioned.

 In AutoCAD LT, you can ensure exact dimensions using several methods. The simplest method is to locate points by snapping to some interval of a *grid*.

Another method is to specify exact *coordinates*. A coordinate identifies a drawing location by indicating a point along an X and Y axis or a distance and angle from another point. You can specify coordinates that are relative to other points or to the drawing's coordinate system.

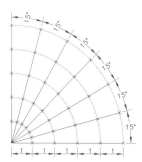

The polar tracking feature displays visual guidelines at specific angles. Polar snap helps you locate points at specified distances.

You can also snap to locations on existing objects, such as an endpoint of an arc, the midpoint of a line, or the center point of a circle.

In this building section, *object snaps* were used to ensure that lines connected perfectly. *Polar tracking* was used to draw lines at correct angles.

 Chapter 6, "Precision Drawing"

When you place your cursor here...

AutoCAD LT automatically snaps to the center point

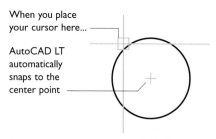

Running object snaps automatically lock onto specific locations on an object, such as the center point of a circle, arc, or ellipse.

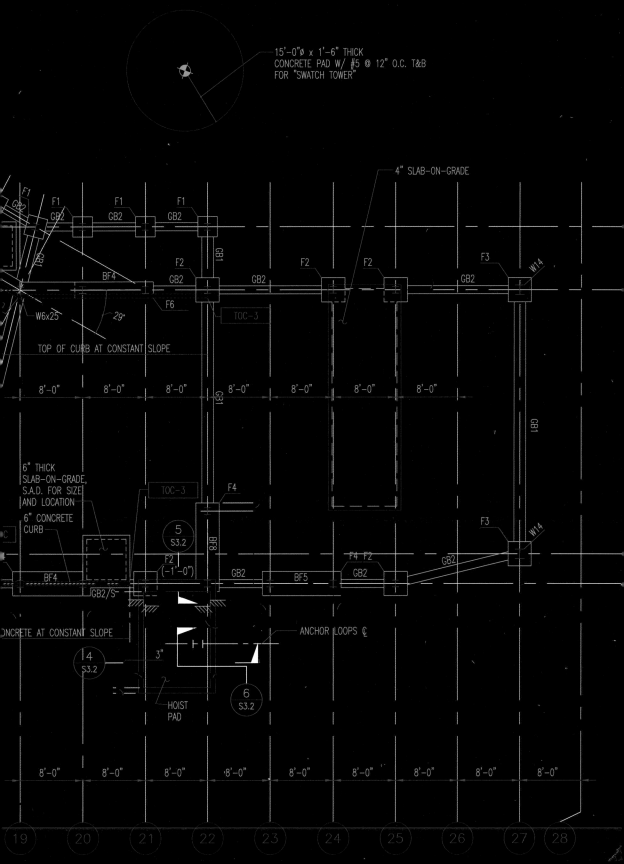

15'-0"Ø x 1'-6" THICK
CONCRETE PAD W/ #5 @ 12" O.C. T&B
FOR "SWATCH TOWER"

4" SLAB-ON-GRADE

F1   F1   F1   F1
GB2   GB2   GB2   GB2

GB1

F2   F2   F2   F3
BF4   GB2   GB2   GB2   W14
F6
GB2

TOC-3

TOP OF CURB AT CONSTANT SLOPE

W6x25   29°

GB1

8'-0"   8'-0"   8'-0"   8'-0"   8'-0"   8'-0"   8'-0"

GB1

6" THICK
SLAB-ON-GRADE,
S.A.D. FOR SIZE
AND LOCATION
                  TOC-3   F4
6" CONCRETE
CURB   5
                             S3.2   F3

                        BF8   F4 F2   F3
                                                       W14
BF4   F2   GB2   GB2 GB2   GB2
          GB2/S- (-1'-0")   BF5

CONCRETE AT CONSTANT SLOPE

ANCHOR LOOPS ℄

4   3"
S3.2   6
                             S3.2

HOIST
PAD

8'-0"   8'-0"   8'-0"   8'-0"   8'-0"   8'-0"   8'-0"   8'-0"   8'-0"

Viewing Your Drawing

The power of CAD makes it easy for you to quickly view different parts of your design at different magnifications.

When you draft on paper and need to work on another section, you must physically move to that area of your drawing.

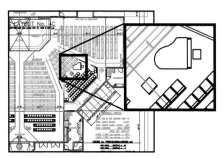

You can zoom out to see more of your design, or zoom in to see more detail.

In CAD, the size and resolution of your computer monitor limit your viewing area. AutoCAD LT viewing methods bypass this limitation.

To do detailed work, you can increase display size by *zooming* in. You can zoom out to display more of the drawing. To move to another section of a drawing, you *pan* the drawing without changing magnification.

You can view several areas of your drawing simultaneously by creating *viewports*. Layout viewports give you the flexibility to arrange views of your model anywhere for plotting. Viewports in model space are tiled (fixed location). They let you work easily on different parts of your model. Changes in one viewport are reflected in the others.

You can zoom and pan in viewports to create the best working conditions. This can be invaluable when working on detailed drawings, such as this church pew layout.

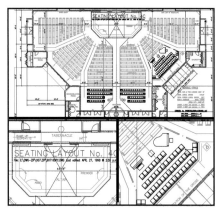

Model space viewports display different portions of your model simultaneously. You can zoom and pan the display in each viewport independently.

Chapter 7, "Changing Views"

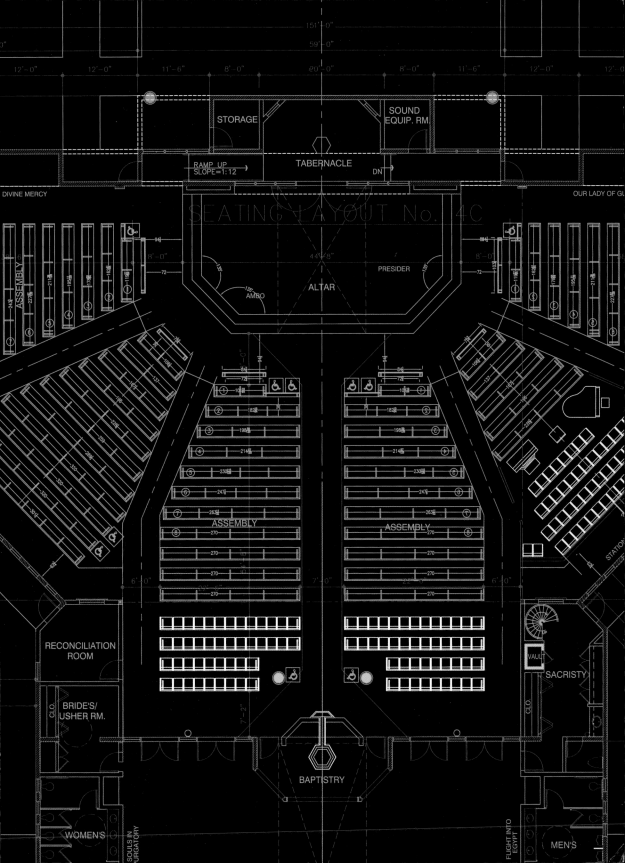

Creating Standard Symbols

Symbols have long been used in manual drafting as a way to represent real-world objects in a simplified way. The ability to create and reuse standard symbols is one of CAD's greatest strengths.

 With manual drafting, you might use a symbol template or printed stickers to draw repetitive landscape, architectural, mechanical, or electrical symbols. This method, however, limits the possible variations of a symbol.

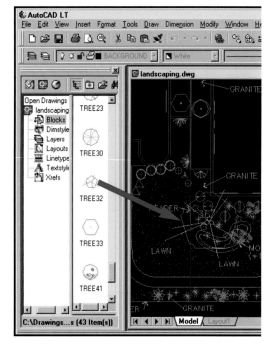

The AutoCAD DesignCenter lets you locate libraries (collections) of blocks that you can drag quickly and easily onto your drawing. You can browse and preview blocks from drawings stored on your computer, on a company network, or on a Web site.

 In AutoCAD LT, you can save time by inserting copies of existing symbols anywhere in your drawing at any rotation, or scale.

When you need to create a custom symbol, you combine several objects into a single named object called a *block*. You then can insert the block as many times as you like into any drawing.

Should a standard symbol change, you can update all instances of a block in your drawing in a single operation, or replace it with a different block.

Standard landscaping symbols are used extensively in this drawing of a residential home floor plan.

 Chapter 10, "Using Blocks and Hatches Repeatedly"

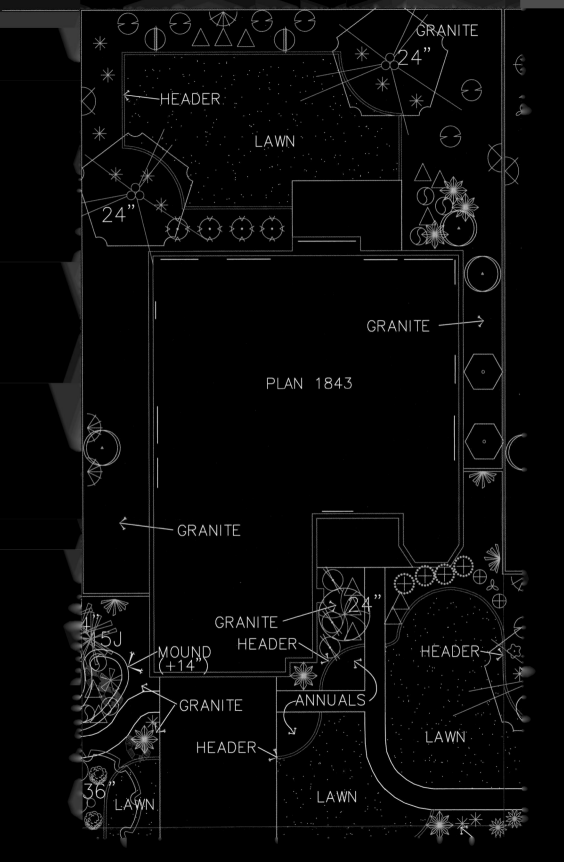

GRANITE

24"

HEADER

LAWN

24"

GRANITE

PLAN 1843

GRANITE

GRANITE

24"

GRANITE
HEADER

HEADER

MOUND
(+14")

15J

ANNUALS

LAWN

GRANITE

HEADER

36"

LAWN

LAWN

Creating Dimensions and Text

Creating accurate dimensions and consistent, legible text is a time-consuming task for the manual drafter. CAD provides ways to streamline this task.

When you work on paper, you typically draw to scale and then add dimensions and annotation. If you resize any part of the drawing, you must erase and then redraw the dimensions. Changing text can often involve relettering the whole paragraph.

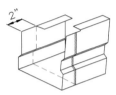

If you make dimensions associative, you can update the dimension size and value automatically when you stretch or scale the dimensioned object.

AutoCAD LT automates the process of creating and changing dimensions and text.

In AutoCAD LT, you can create dimension styles that facilitate standardization. When information changes, you can easily revise text, including its content, font, size, spacing, and rotation.

Virtually all standard dimensioning types are provided in AutoCAD LT: linear, radial, ordinate, angular, baseline, and more. You can dimension most objects by simply selecting them.

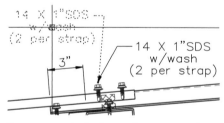

You can create leader lines with an associated callout. If you move the the callout, the leader is adjusted automatically.

In this detail drawing of a gutter, text, leaders, and dimensions are used to describe the required hardware.

Chapter 11, "Adding Text" and Chapter 12, "Dimensioning"

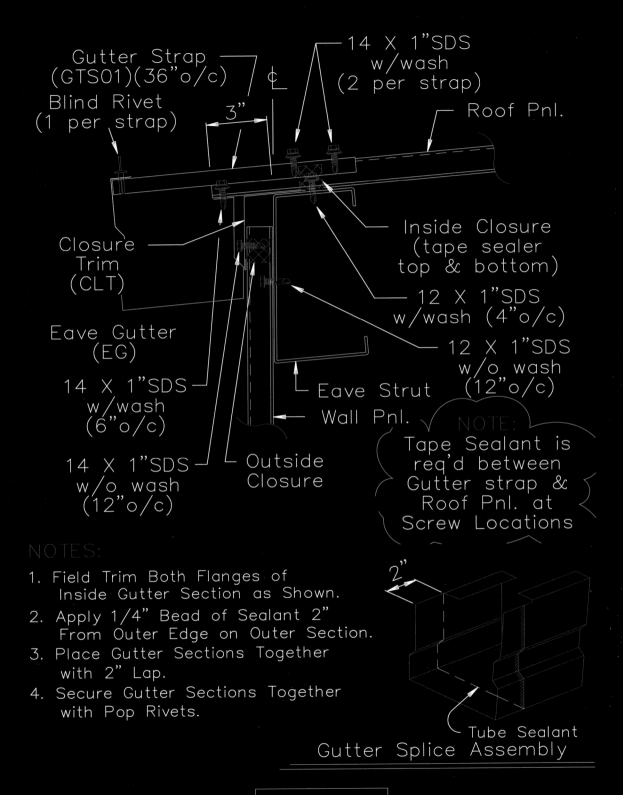

Gutter Strap
(GTS01)(36"o/c)

Blind Rivet
(1 per strap)

¢

3"

14 X 1"SDS
w/wash
(2 per strap)

Roof Pnl.

Inside Closure
(tape sealer
top & bottom)

12 X 1"SDS
w/wash (4"o/c)

12 X 1"SDS
w/o wash
(12"o/c)

Closure
Trim
(CLT)

Eave Gutter
(EG)

14 X 1"SDS
w/wash
(6"o/c)

14 X 1"SDS
w/o wash
(12"o/c)

Outside
Closure

Eave Strut

Wall Pnl.

NOTE:
Tape Sealant is
req'd between
Gutter strap &
Roof Pnl. at
Screw Locations

NOTES:
1. Field Trim Both Flanges of
   Inside Gutter Section as Shown.
2. Apply 1/4" Bead of Sealant 2"
   From Outer Edge on Outer Section.
3. Place Gutter Sections Together
   with 2" Lap.
4. Secure Gutter Sections Together
   with Pop Rivets.

2"

Tube Sealant

Gutter Splice Assembly

PL105

Modifying Your Drawing

Revisions are a part of any drawing project. Whether you work on paper or with CAD, you will need to modify your drawing in some way.

 On paper you must manually erase and redraw to make revisions to your drawing.

 AutoCAD LT eliminates tedious manual editing by providing a wealth of editing tools. If you need to copy all or part of an object, you don't have to redraw it. If you need to remove an object, you can erase it with a few clicks of the mouse. And if you make an error, you can quickly undo your actions.

Once you draw an object, you never need to redraw it. You can modify existing objects by mirroring, rotating, scaling, stretching, trimming, and more. You can change the properties of an object, such as linetype, lineweight, color, and layer, at any time.

These before-and-after drawings show some typical edits to a house elevation. The *revision cloud* feature is used to mark areas of change.

 Chapter 9, "Making Modifications"

If you stretch an object ...

the hatch adjusts automatically.

Incorporating Other Drawings

Sharing content is fundamental to managing a drawing project. For example, on a team project, you might need to incorporate information from other drawings into your drawing.

With manual drafting, reusing information from another drawing requires photocopying that section and pasting it into your drawing. This is most commonly done using adhesive-backed transparencies.

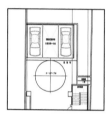

If you're working on a floor plan ...

With AutoCAD LT, you can reference all or part of another drawing by creating an external reference (xref). *Xrefs* let you incorporate other drawings without making the data part of your current drawing. This can be useful for displaying standard components or for checking accuracy or interference with another drawing.

Xrefs are updated automatically each time you open your drawing, thereby keeping you up-to-date with revisions.

Xrefs can be located on your own computer or your company's network. You can also access them over the Internet using AutoCAD DesignCenter.

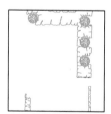

and you want to see how the landscaping plan looks...

In this floor plan, the master drawing contains the roadway, building, and parking lot. The landscape drawing is externally referenced.

Chapter 13, "Information Sharing"

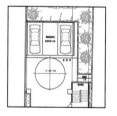

you can superimpose it on your drawing as an external reference.

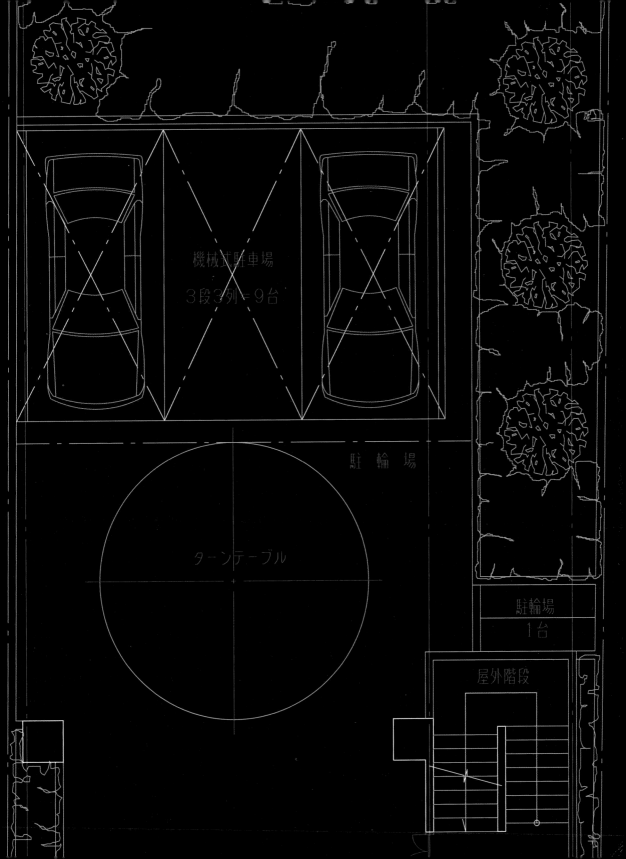

機械式駐車場

3段3列=9台

駐輪場

ターンテーブル

駐輪場

1台

屋外階段

CREDITS

Building Section and
Details
DeMello & Associates,
USA

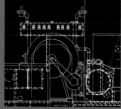

Press Installation
Len DeMario,
Chesnut Engineering, USA

Traffic Signal Design
Dept. of Public Works,
City of San Bernardino,
USA

Swatch Pavilion
Peter Balint, Ove Arup &
Partners
USA

Church Pew Layout
Walter Jacobi and Sons,
Inc.
USA

Eave and Gutter Detail
Lewis Ellis,
Kirby Building Systems,
USA

Family Home Elevation
Mensch Und Maschine,
Germany

Cottage Plan and Elevation
Geoff Martin,
Phillips Structures Ltd.,
England

Electric Train
Ray Parker,
BC Transit,
Canada

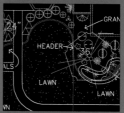

Landscaping Design
Marc McKeown,
McKeown Inc,
USA

Home Floor Plan
Ikeshita Sekkei Co. Ltd.,
Japan

Installing AutoCAD LT

2

This chapter lists the hardware and software required to run AutoCAD LT® and describes how to install AutoCAD LT. If you already have a version of AutoCAD LT installed on your computer, you can save and reuse most of your customized settings.

In this chapter

- System Requirements
- Installing AutoCAD LT
- Restoring Your Default Web Browser
- Upgrading from a Previous Release
- Reinstalling AutoCAD LT
- Uninstalling AutoCAD LT

System Requirements

To run AutoCAD LT, the following resources are required or supported.

Hardware (Required)

- Intel Pentium processor, 133 MHz or higher, or compatible processor
- VGA video display (800 by 600 or higher resolution required)
- CD-ROM driver for initial installation and running *Learning Assistance*
- Windows-supported display adapter
- Mouse or other pointing device (wheel mouse recommended)

Hardware (Optional)

- Printer or plotter
- Wintab-compatible digitizing tablet

Software

- Windows 2000, Windows NT® 4.0, Windows® 95b, or Windows 98. It is recommended that you install and run AutoCAD LT on an operating system in the same language as your AutoCAD LT software or on an English version of the operating system.
- *WHIP!*® Browser Accessory 4.0. DWF files are designed to be viewed on the Internet or company intranets using a Web browser. *WHIP!* is available as a Netscape Navigator plug-in and as a Microsoft® Internet Explorer ActiveX™ control. For information about downloading *WHIP!*, go to *http://www3.autodesk.com/adsk/section/0,,163301,00.html*.

RAM and Hard Disk Space

- 64 MB of RAM minimum
- 120 MB minimum of hard disk space
- 45 MB for Microsoft Internet Explorer (MSIE) 5.0 on your system drive (if MSIE is not already present)
- 64 MB of disk swap space minimum, 100 MB recommended
- 5 MB of free disk space during installation only (this space is used for temporary files that are removed when installation is complete)

Additional RAM and hard disk space may be required if you are using Windows 2000. For MSIE 5.0, an additional 10 MB to 14 MB of space may be required for files installed in the *System* folder; this space does not need to be on the same drive as the program folder where you launch AutoCAD LT.

Installing AutoCAD LT

These instructions describe installing AutoCAD LT for a single user.

Preparing for AutoCAD LT Installation

Make sure that you have write permission in the following locations:

- Folder where you are installing AutoCAD LT
- Windows *System* folder
- System registry

If you use Windows 2000 or Windows NT, you need Administrator rights to install AutoCAD LT. You must have permission to write to the necessary system registry sections. See the information about User Manager in the Windows 2000 or Windows NT online Help, which you can access from the Start menu on the taskbar.

NOTE To use AutoCAD LT 2000i with the Windows 2000 operating system, you should have either Power User or Administrator rights. Failure to assign these rights causes AutoCAD LT 2000i to perform incorrectly.

Ensure that you meet the minimum system requirements as specified in the previous section.

Installing AutoCAD LT for a Single User

The following procedure installs AutoCAD LT for a single user. You can cancel the setup process at any time by pressing Cancel.

NOTE Some virus protection packages may slow your installation.

To install AutoCAD LT for a single user

1 Close any open applications.
2 Insert the CD into the CD-ROM drive.

- Autorun begins the installation process as soon as you insert the CD unless you hold down the SHIFT key while you insert the CD.
- If you have turned off Autorun, or if you have installed AutoCAD LT from the CD before, you must designate the CD-ROM drive. From the Start menu, choose Run, designate the CD-ROM drive, and enter **setup**. For example, enter **d:\setup**.

3 In the Welcome to the AutoCAD LT 2000i Installation Wizard, choose Next.

4 Review the Autodesk software license agreement. You must accept this agreement to complete the AutoCAD LT installation. To accept, choose I Accept, and then choose Next.

5 Enter your user information and choose Next. Follow the prompts.

If the installation program finds a previous release of AutoCAD LT registered on your system, it prompts you to specify whether you want to install AutoCAD LT 2000i in a separate directory, or upgrade. For more information about upgrading, see page 40.

6 Specify the type of installation you want, and then choose Next:

- *Typical* installs the following files:

  Program files (executables, menus, toolbars, templates, TrueType fonts, and additional support files)

  Samples (sample drawings and images)

  Support files

  Help (online Help files, What's New, and support files)

- *Compact* installs the executables, support files, and online Help only.
- *Custom* installs the files you specify. By default, the Custom installation option installs all AutoCAD LT components. Deselect the AutoCAD LT components you do *not* want to install. For example, you can choose not to install the folder containing sample drawings. The Custom installation can also include an option to install an alternate dictionary to check spelling in an additional language.
- *Full* installs all application features, including the French-Canadian dictionary.

NOTE Choosing Typical installs Microsoft NetMeeting 3.01.

---

7 Choose Next to accept the default installation directory for AutoCAD LT, *C:\Program Files\AutoCAD LT 2000i*. Otherwise, choose Browse, select a different installation directory, and then choose Next.

8 Choose Next to start the installation.

9 When prompted, restart your computer to complete the installation. Display the *Readme* file to read late-breaking news about AutoCAD LT 2000i.

Restoring Your Default Web Browser

Online Help requires Microsoft Internet Explorer (MSIE) version 5.0 or higher to run. The installation program detects this Web browser on your computer. If the appropriate software is not detected, the installation program installs MSIE version 5.0. If you attempt to access online Help from the Help menu, and the appropriate files or version of MSIE are not properly installed on your computer, a warning message prompts you to run the installation program again.

NOTE All online Help files are installed on your hard drive. You do not need to access the Web to view Help.

If MSIE 5.*x* was not previously installed on your machine, MSIE automatically becomes your default browser when you install AutoCAD LT. However, you have the option of retaining your original browser. When you retain your original browser, MSIE 5.*x* is still available for online Help.

To restore your default Web browser

1 After installation, restart your computer if you have not already done so.
2 Launch your default Internet browser. A dialog box asks if you would like to restore your original browser. This example shows the dialog box for Netscape Navigator.

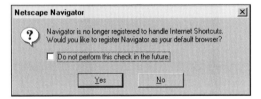

3 Choose Yes to restore your default browser.

Upgrading from a Previous Release

Installing the upgrade version of AutoCAD LT 2000i requires that

- You previously installed a full commercial release of AutoCAD LT.
- The upgrade version is in the same language as the installed version.

The installation program searches for the AutoCAD LT executable file *(aclt.exe)*. If a dialog box warns you that a valid executable file could not be found, click Browse to search for the file. If the search is successful, the installation program continues as outlined in the procedure for installing AutoCAD LT on page 37.

Overwriting a Previous Version of AutoCAD LT

Your upgrade installation program interacts differently with previous versions of AutoCAD LT depending on the version. Please see the following table for guidelines.

Upgrade compatibility guidelines	
Upgrading	**Effect of installation**
AutoCAD LT 2000, AutoCAD LT 98, and AutoCAD LT 97	Can exist on the same operating system. You can choose to upgrade the previous version or to install AutoCAD LT 2000i in a *different* folder if you do not want to uninstall the older version.
AutoCAD LT 95, AutoCAD LT 1 and 2	Can exist on the same operating system. Installing AutoCAD LT 2000i in the same folder does not affect these versions because they cannot be upgraded to AutoCAD LT 2000i.

If you install the upgrade version of AutoCAD LT 2000i in the *same* program folder as your previous version of AutoCAD LT, you may lose customized files, such as menu files. To prevent loss, copy all customized files to a temporary folder before installing AutoCAD LT 2000i.

Reusing Customizable Support Files

If you have customized support files from previous releases of AutoCAD LT, you can reuse the information in AutoCAD LT 2000i. For example, you can reuse customized hatch patterns previously saved in the hatch definition file *(aclt.pat)* by copying and pasting the customized definitions into the newly installed file using a text editor.

NOTE You should *not* replace the newly installed support files with versions from a previous release of AutoCAD LT.

The following table lists the support files you can reuse.

Customizable support files you can reuse with AutoCAD LT 2000i	
File name	**Description**
aclt.pat	Library file that contains standard hatch pattern definitions
acltiso.pat	Library file that contains metric hatch pattern definitions
aclt.lin	Library file that contains standard linetype definitions
acltiso.lin	Library file that contains metric linetype definitions
aclt.mnu	Menu template file; contains menu definitions and comments and is generally used for reference
aclt.mns	Source menu file; can be customized by using a text editor
aclt.pgp	Program parameters file; an ASCII text file that stores command alias definitions
aclt.unt	Unit definition file; contains units and equivalencies
fontmap.ps	File that maps PostScript to TrueType fonts when you open a drawing that uses PostScript fonts
sample.cus	Custom dictionary for use in checking spelling

Reinstalling AutoCAD LT

You can change your AutoCAD LT installation in two ways. Adding and removing features is a good way to add files that were not previously installed or to decrease the amount of disk space used by AutoCAD LT. Reinstalling is a good way to replace files that you have accidentally deleted or altered. You use the Windows Control Panel to change your installation.

Adding and Removing Components

You can add and remove components at any time by double-clicking Add/Remove Programs in the Windows Control Panel, selecting AutoCAD LT 2000i, and choosing Add/Remove. After selecting Add or Remove Features in the AutoCAD LT 2000i Setup dialog box, select the components that you want to add, clear the components that you do *not* want to be available, and then proceed with the installation by following the prompts. This option is available only if you have already installed AutoCAD LT from the CD.

Reinstalling AutoCAD LT

You can reinstall files by choosing Reinstall AutoCAD LT 2000i in the AutoCAD LT 2000i Setup dialog box. This option is available only if you have already installed AutoCAD LT from the CD. It reinstalls all or some of the components you previously installed in the program folder you originally specified.

Uninstalling AutoCAD LT

You can uninstall AutoCAD LT 2000i by double-clicking Add/Remove Programs in the Windows Control Panel and choosing Remove AutoCAD LT 2000i in the AutoCAD LT 2000i Setup dialog box. Uninstalling removes all of the program files that were part of the original installation as well as program components that were added later. Files that were created after installation of AutoCAD LT are not removed. This includes *aclt2000i.cfg* and any drawing files that you have created in the *AutoCAD LT 2000i* folder tree. You can manually delete these files after uninstalling AutoCAD LT.

When AutoCAD LT has been successfully uninstalled, be sure to restart your computer to ensure that any files that may have been in use by your operating system are properly uninstalled. Choose Cancel if you don't want to restart your computer immediately.

ONLINE HELP CUSTOMIZE, MENULOAD, OPTIONS

Graphics area. The area of the AutoCAD LT window where you create and edit drawings.

Standard toolbar.

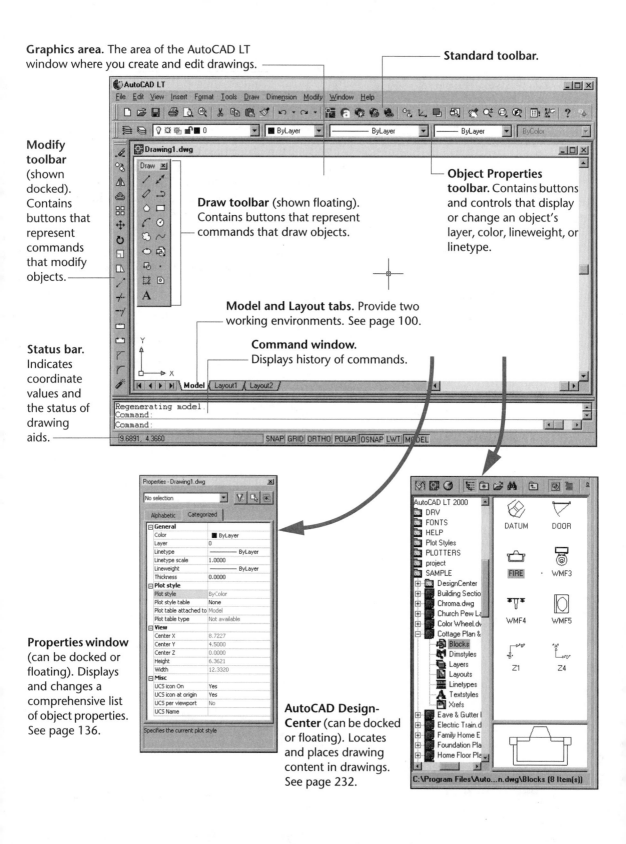

Modify toolbar (shown docked). Contains buttons that represent commands that modify objects.

Draw toolbar (shown floating). Contains buttons that represent commands that draw objects.

Object Properties toolbar. Contains buttons and controls that display or change an object's layer, color, lineweight, or linetype.

Model and Layout tabs. Provide two working environments. See page 100.

Status bar. Indicates coordinate values and the status of drawing aids.

Command window. Displays history of commands.

Properties window (can be docked or floating). Displays and changes a comprehensive list of object properties. See page 136.

AutoCAD Design-Center (can be docked or floating). Locates and places drawing content in drawings. See page 232.

Understanding the Workspace

3

This chapter explains the AutoCAD LT® interface, including the ways you issue commands to get work done. You can issue commands by choosing options from menus or toolbars or by typing on the command line.

When you first open AutoCAD LT, the screen contains the menu bar at the top, the status bar at the bottom, the graphics area, the command window, and several toolbars. You can display additional toolbars as needed.

As you work, you may want to open AutoCAD® Design-Center™ and the Properties window. Later chapters cover these useful windows. The Model and Layout tabs are also covered in a later chapter.

In this chapter

- Using Pointing Devices
- Choosing Commands from Menus
- Starting Commands with Toolbar Buttons
- Entering Commands on the Command Line
- Exploring the Interface with a Mouse
- Working with Commands

Using Pointing Devices

You can control AutoCAD LT with a wide range of pointing devices, such as a standard two-button mouse, a wheel mouse, or a digitizing tablet.

Configuring the Pointing Device

After you install AutoCAD LT, you don't need to configure the mouse or digitizer; AutoCAD LT uses the current Windows®system pointing device. To change the current pointing device, use the options on the System tab in the Options dialog box. You can also control whether AutoCAD LT accepts input from only a digitizer or from both a digitizer and a mouse.

pick
button

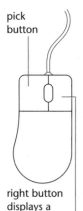

right button
displays a
shortcut
menu or
issues ENTER

Using the Mouse

You can choose menu options and toolbar buttons by clicking them with a mouse. You can also use the mouse to draw, select, or modify objects on the screen.

On a two-button mouse, the left button is usually the *pick* button, used to specify points or select objects on the screen. With AutoCAD LT, you can set the right button (the return button) either to display a *shortcut menu* or to serve as an alternative to pressing ENTER.

A wheel mouse is a two-button mouse with a small wheel between the buttons. This wheel can be rotated by discrete values or pressed down. You can use the wheel to zoom and pan your drawing quickly.

Using the Tablet

You can use a digitizing tablet to select frequently used commands, to select objects on the screen, or to draw. The tablet's pointing device, which you use for selection, can be a *puck* or a *stylus*. The crosshairs on the screen follow the movement of the pointing device in the screen pointing area of the tablet.

You can also use a tablet to digitize drawings by tracing objects into an AutoCAD LT drawing using coordinates that relate to the original drawing. For example, if you are working with a drawing that was originally prepared by hand, you can convert that drawing for storage and editing in AutoCAD LT by laying it on the tablet and tracing it with the puck or stylus.

To digitize a drawing, you *calibrate*, or align, the tablet with the paper drawing's coordinate system. If the paper drawing is too big to fit on the tablet, you can enter the drawing in pieces, making sure each piece is correctly aligned. For more information about configuring and calibrating tablets, see appendix B, page 275.

AutoCAD LT provides a special input mode called Tablet mode. In Tablet mode, the active area of your tablet coincides with the current display. When Tablet mode is off, the screen pointing area of your tablet coincides with specific coordinates in your drawing; the portion of your drawing that you are currently viewing is irrelevant. Any command that requires you to select objects with the pointing device works in Tablet mode.

NOTE The first 10 buttons of a multibutton pointing device are automatically assigned by AutoCAD LT. However, you can reassign all but the pick button by modifying the menu file *(aclt.mnu)*.

To get started		
Action	Menu	Dialog box tab
Changing the pointing device	Tools ➤ Options	System
Turning on shortcut menus	Tools ➤ Options	User Preferences

ONLINE HELP Mouse, OPTIONS, TABMODE

Choosing Commands from Menus

You can choose commands from several kinds of menus in AutoCAD LT:

- *Pull-down menus* are available from the menu bar at the top of the AutoCAD LT window.
- *Object Snap menu* is displayed when you hold down SHIFT and click the right (return) button on the pointing device.
- *Shortcut menus* are displayed when you press the right (return) button on the pointing device.

Pull-Down Menus

You can choose pull-down menu commands in *any* of the following ways:

- After you click the menu name, click the command to choose it.
- Hold down ALT and then enter the underlined letter in the menu name. For example, hold down ALT and press F (ALT+F) to open the File menu. Then press A to choose Save As.
- Use shortcut keys to choose menu commands directly. For example, press CTRL+P to choose Print. Available shortcut keys are displayed opposite the command names on the menus.

Object Snap Menu

The Object Snap menu lists object snaps, which facilitate precision drawing. See page 114 for information about snapping to precise points.

Hold down the SHIFT key and right-click your pointing device to display the Object Snap menu. On a two-button mouse, the return button is usually the right button.

You can customize the Object Snap menu, as you can all AutoCAD LT menus, by editing the *aclt.mnu* file.

Shortcut Menus

Using shortcut menus helps you concentrate on your work. You right-click to display related commands, rather than going to a toolbar or pull-down menu. The commands in the shortcut menu change depending on where you right-click. The basic types of shortcut menus are listed below.

- *Edit-mode menu* is displayed when you right-click with objects selected but no command in progress.
- *Default menu* is displayed when you right-click in the graphics area with no command in progress and no objects selected.

- *Command-mode menu* is displayed when you right-click with a command in progress.
- *Available toolbars menu* is displayed when you right-click a toolbar.
- *Command history* is displayed when you right-click on the command line.

NOTE You can use the Options dialog box to change how right-clicking works. You can make right-clicking equivalent to pressing ENTER. Displaying shortcut menus is the default option. See page 106 for more information.

To get started			
Action	**Menu**	**Dialog box tab**	**Keyboard**
Turning on shortcut menus	Tools ➤ Options	User Preferences	
Ending commands			ENTER or SPACEBAR
Repeating commands			ENTER
Canceling commands			ESC

ONLINE HELP Menu, OPTIONS

Starting Commands with Toolbar Buttons

Toolbars contain buttons that start commands. When you move the pointing device over a button, a *tooltip* displays its name.

Using the Standard Toolbar and Flyouts

The Standard toolbar at the top of the graphics area is displayed by default. It contains buttons for frequently used AutoCAD LT commands such as Pan and Zoom, as well as standard commands such as Open, Save, and Print. Buttons with a small black triangle in the lower-right corner extend to display related commands or options. With the cursor over the toolbar button, hold down the left mouse button to display these flyout toolbars. The button you choose from the flyout replaces the original button on the toolbar.

Docking, Resizing, and Floating Toolbars

A docked toolbar is attached to any edge of the graphics area. It cannot be resized and does not overlap the graphics area. You can float a toolbar by dragging it anywhere in the graphics area of the AutoCAD LT window, and you can resize it by dragging any edge.

Displaying and Customizing Toolbars

AutoCAD LT offers many more toolbars than are displayed by default when you start the program. Using the Customize dialog box, you can display multiple toolbars, resize them, and control whether tooltips are displayed. You can also customize existing toolbars and create your own toolbars.

Click here to display the toolbar.

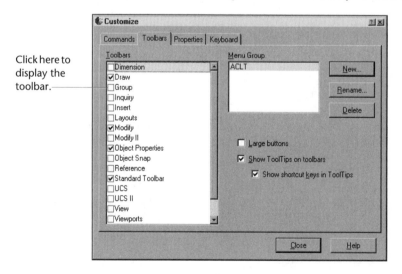

Using Toolbar Buttons to Correct Mistakes

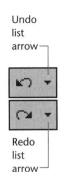

Undo
list
arrow

Redo
list
arrow

Two Standard toolbar buttons reverse mistakes in your drawings.

■ *Undo*. You can backtrack actions taken in the current AutoCAD LT session. For example, click Undo to delete a circle that you just created.
■ *Redo*. You can reinstate the actions that you backtracked with Undo. For example, click redo to re-create a circle that you just undid.

You can use the Undo and Redo lists to reverse more than one action at a time. Drag to select the actions and click to undo or redo those actions.

NOTE Not all of the menu commands are represented by toolbar buttons.

To get started		
Action	Menu	Keyboard
Displaying toolbars	View ▶ Toolbars	
Ending commands		ENTER or SPACEBAR
Repeating commands		ENTER or SPACEBAR
Canceling commands		ESC

ONLINE HELP TOOLBAR, CUSTOMIZE, UNDO, REDO

Entering Commands on the Command Line

You can initiate AutoCAD LT commands on the command line instead of using toolbars or menus. Additionally, some commands *must* be completed on the command line, regardless of how they are started.

Starting Commands and Responding to Prompts

When you enter commands, AutoCAD LT displays either a set of options or a dialog box. For example, when you enter the CIRCLE command, the following prompt is displayed on the command line:

Specify center point for circle or [3P/2P/Ttr (tan tan radius)]:

The current option is described before the square brackets. To accept it, enter coordinate values, or use the pointing device to click a center point on the screen. To choose a different option, enter the capitalized letters in the option name—for example, entering **3P** chooses the Three-Point option.

Use the following practices when working on the command line:

- *To execute commands*, press SPACEBAR or ENTER.
- *To repeat commands*, press SPACEBAR or ENTER, or right-click in the graphics area and select the previous command from the shortcut menu.
- *To cancel commands in progress*, press ESC.

Viewing the Command History

By default, the command window is docked below the graphics area. If text that is entered becomes longer than the width of the command line, the window pops up in front of the command line to show the full text of the line. You can resize the window vertically by dragging the splitter bar, which is located on the inside edge of the window. You can also press F2 to display a separate text window to view a long list of commands or commands such as LIST, which have text output.

splitter bar—

Reissuing Commands

You can reissue any command used during the current AutoCAD LT session by accessing it in the command history. Highlighting the command in the text window and pressing ENTER starts the command again.

Using Two Commands at the Same Time

Many commands can be used *transparently*, which means they can be entered on the command line while you are using another command. Transparent commands include commands such as ZOOM, which change drawings views, or drawing aids such as SNAP or GRID. To use a command transparently, you must precede it with an apostrophe (').

Of course, you can also choose transparent ZOOM and PAN commands from AutoCAD LT toolbars and menus.

Switching from Dialog Box to Command Line

Some functions are available both on the command line and in a dialog box. For many commands, you can force AutoCAD LT to display prompts instead of a dialog box by entering a hyphen before the command to suppress the dialog box. For example, entering **-layer**, instead of **layer**, displays command line options equivalent to those presented in the dialog box.

NOTE Some commands have abbreviated names or *aliases*. For example, you can enter **z** as an alias for ZOOM. See appendix C, page 291, or the Quick Reference card for information.

ONLINE HELP Command, MULTIPLE

Exploring the Interface with a Mouse

Most AutoCAD LT users choose a mouse as their pointing device. This topic helps you learn the AutoCAD LT interface while practicing with the mouse.

Moving the Cursor

1 Move your mouse around the AutoCAD LT window.

   Notice that the pointer on the screen changes from crosshairs while in the graphics area to an arrow when it's over menus and toolbars. Note also that the pointer changes to an I-beam when it's in the command window.

2 Move the pointer over the Standard toolbar at the top of the graphics area.

   As you leave the cursor over a toolbar button for a few seconds, notice a pop-up label, called a *tooltip*, that identifies the button.

3 On the status bar, click the coordinate display several times and watch how it changes each time you click it. When the text is dimmed, no information is available. When activated, the coordinate display indicates the exact location, or *coordinate* values, of the crosshairs on the screen. For more information, see page 112.

coordinate display — `8.1134, 4.8862`

4 Watch the coordinate display as you move the mouse.

   Notice how the numbers in the coordinate display change.

Docking and Undocking Toolbars

1 Move the pointer over a blank area on any toolbar. Then, as you hold down the pick button, drag the toolbar around the screen to reposition it.

2 Dock the toolbar by dragging it to a docking location at the top, bottom, or either side of the drawing area. When the outline of the toolbar appears in the docking area, release the pick button.

Constraining the Cursor

1 Find the Snap button on the status bar and click it with the pick button on your mouse (by default, the left button).

   Notice that the button changes to indicate that Snap has been turned on.

2 Move the pointer around the screen while Snap is turned on.

   Observe that the pointer seems to adhere, or "snap," to points at equal intervals on the screen. You can change these intervals.

Displaying Shortcut Menus

1 From the Tools menu, choose Options to display the Options dialog box.

2 On the User Preferences tab, choose Right-Click Customization.

3 In the Right-Click Customization dialog box, make sure that the Default Mode, Edit Mode, and Command Mode options are set to display a shortcut menu. Choose Apply & Close to exit the Right-Click Customization dialog box. Then choose OK to exit the Options dialog box.

4 At the Command prompt, place the cursor over the graphics area, the command window, or a toolbar and right-click the mouse.

   Note the shortcut menu that is displayed.

5 Place the cursor over a different area in the AutoCAD LT window and right-click again.

   Observe that the context-sensitive shortcut menu changes depending on where you right-click.

Displaying the Object Snap Menu

1 Enter any command that prompts you to specify a point. For example, from the Draw menu, choose Line.

2 At the Specify First Point prompt, hold down SHIFT and right-click.

   The Object Snap menu, which is used for precise placement of points, is displayed

3 Press ESC to cancel the command.

Working with Commands

After you start a command, you might take one or more of these actions:

- Use the pointing device to draw an object in the graphics area.
- Select options in a dialog box.
- Respond to prompts displayed on the command line.

Because AutoCAD LT is very flexible, you can work in the way that feels most comfortable to you. This topic uses a simple example to illustrate how to work with AutoCAD LT commands. It tells you how to draw a line by starting the LINE command with a menu, with a toolbar, or on the command line.

Using a Menu to Draw a Line

1 Move the cursor to the menu bar and choose the Draw menu by clicking the word Draw.

   A pull-down menu lists the Draw menu options.

2 Click the word Line.

   Notice that the command line now displays a prompt: Specify First Point.

3 Click anywhere in the graphics area to locate a point.

   The prompt changes: Specify Next Point or [Undo].

4 Click anywhere else in the graphics area to indicate the endpoint of the line segment.

5 Create a second line segment by clicking again to locate another point.

6 Press ENTER to end the LINE command.

NOTE You can right-click and use the shortcut menu to repeat your last command. For example, you can start another line by choosing Repeat Line from the shortcut menu.

Using a Button on a Toolbar to Draw a Line

1 On the Draw toolbar, choose Line by positioning the cursor over the Line button. Then click the pointing device to start the LINE command.

2 Follow steps 3 through 6 above to draw two line segments.

Using the Command Line to Draw a Line

1 At the Command prompt, enter **line**.

2 At the Specify First Point prompt, enter **5,5** to locate the beginning of the line.

3 At the Specify Next Point or [Undo] prompt, enter **8,5** to locate the end of the line segment.

The Specify Next Point or [Undo] prompt repeats so you can continue to draw segments until you end the LINE command.

NOTE Enter **u** to undo the last action without ending the command.

---

4 Enter **5,8** to create the second line segment. Then enter **c** (Close) and press ENTER.

AutoCAD LT connects the endpoint of the second line segment with the start point of the first segment and ends the LINE command.

5 At the Command prompt, enter **z** (Zoom). Then enter **e** (Extents) to ensure that the entire drawing is displayed in the graphics area.

6 On the status bar, click the coordinate display to activate it.

7 Move the cursor over the endpoint of the first line segment. Then move the cursor over the endpoint of the second line segment.

Observe how the numbers in the coordinate display change.

NOTE By pressing ENTER, you can repeat the last command. For example, you can start another line by pressing ENTER after ending the LINE command.

You will learn to draw circles and polygons.

You will learn to load various linetypes and to organize linetypes and colors by drawing layer.

Ø1.10

You will learn to fillet corners and trim away excess lines.

6.99

1.22

3.00

3.94

R0.50

1.97

.79

AUTODESK, INC.
BY: LAURA N.

You will learn to draw and offset lines.

You will learn to create dimensions and text.

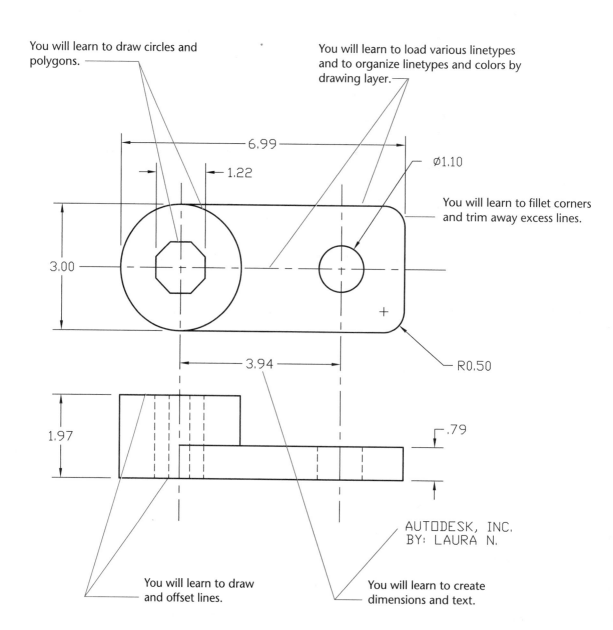

The drawing you create in this tutorial

The CAD Drawing Tutorial

4

This tutorial provides an introduction to creating and plotting a simple drawing. Follow the step-by-step procedures—from how to start the drawing process to how to plot the final output on paper. You will begin with a hand-drawn sketch.

AutoCAD LT® provides several methods for drawing objects. This exercise demonstrates only one approach to creating the drawing shown opposite.

For detailed information about some of the commands you will use, see online Help or the appropriate sections in this guide. See the Quick Reference card for illustrations of the AutoCAD LT toolbars.

In this chapter

- Preparing for the Tutorial
- Setting Up the Drawing Area
- Creating and Editing Objects at Full Size
- Dimensioning the Drawing
- Adding Annotation
- Plotting the Drawing

Preparing for the Tutorial

This tutorial guides you through the fundamental procedures to produce drawings with AutoCAD LT. In order for the tutorial to run smoothly, use the information below to set up the AutoCAD LT workspace. This part of the tutorial takes about 10 minutes to complete. First, you start AutoCAD LT.

To start AutoCAD LT

1 On the Windows®taskbar, click Start, and then choose Programs.
2 Choose AutoCAD LT 2000i ➤ AutoCAD LT 2000i.
3 Note the information in the Active Assistance window.

    The Active Assistance information changes as you work, providing dynamic context-sensitive help for the task at hand.

4 Close the Today window.

Setting Right-Click to Display Shortcut Menus

You will use shortcut menus in this tutorial. By default, AutoCAD LT displays a context-sensitive shortcut menu when you right-click. The other alternative, which you will not use in this tutorial, makes right-clicking equivalent to pressing ENTER.

To turn on shortcut menus

1 From the Tools menu, choose Options to display the Options dialog box.
2 On the User Preferences tab, choose Right-Click Customization.
3 In the Right-Click Customization dialog box, under Default Mode and under Edit Mode, select Shortcut Menu. Under Command Mode, select Shortcut Menu: Always Enabled.
4 Choose Apply & Close. Then choose OK.

Displaying the Toolbars You Need

Make sure that certain toolbars are displayed. When you first install the program, AutoCAD LT displays the Standard, Object Properties, Draw, and Modify toolbars by default. However, they may have been turned off.

To display toolbars

1 Right-click any toolbar button to display a list of available toolbars. A check mark indicates that the toolbar is selected.
2 In the toolbar list, make sure that Draw, Modify, Object Properties, and Standard Toolbar are selected. Click an item in the list to select it.

Setting Running Object Snaps and AutoSnap

For the purposes of this exercise, turn off any object snaps you may have set previously. You will turn on selected object snap settings later in this tutorial. Now you turn on the settings that help you identify the object snaps when you use them. For example, turning on AutoSnap tooltips causes AutoCAD LT to display the name of object snap locations, such as the midpoints of lines or the centers of circles, when you move the mouse close to them.

To set running object snaps and AutoSnap

1 From the Tools menu, choose Drafting Settings to display the Drafting Settings dialog box.

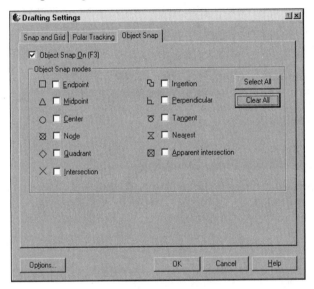

2 On the Object Snap tab in the Drafting Settings dialog box, select Clear All.

3 Click the Options button to display the Options dialog box.

4 On the Drafting tab, under AutoSnap Settings, make sure that Marker, Magnet, and Display AutoSnap Tooltip are selected.

5 Choose OK to exit each dialog box.

For information about snapping to precise points on objects, see page 114.

Setting Up the Drawing Area

Before you begin drawing on paper, you need to set up your drawing area by deciding where each specific plan or detail will go, what type of units and scale you want to use, and what size paper you need.

In the AutoCAD LT setup wizard, you specify the type of units you want to use, but you draw at "full scale." For example, a single unit in your drawing could represent an inch or a kilometer.

You also define an imaginary boundary, called the drawing limits, that is usually slightly larger than the intended drawing. The drawing limits control the area covered by a grid, which helps you visualize the size of the drawing.

The first exercise sets up the drawing area in AutoCAD LT. It takes about 20 minutes to complete. You will

- Set the type of unit you want to use
- Establish the drawing area by setting the limits
- Set up the drawing aids by setting grid and snap intervals
- Separate the drawing into components by creating layers
- Load linetypes for different types of lines

Beginning a New Drawing

Typically, you might start with a hand-drawn sketch of what you will draw in AutoCAD LT.

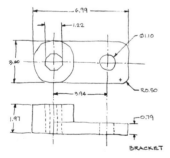

One easy way to start a new drawing in AutoCAD LT 2000i is to use the Quick Setup wizard. In this exercise, you use the Quick Setup wizard to establish the unit type and the general size of your drawing area.

To begin a new drawing

1 From the Tools menu, choose Today to display the Today window.

2 On the Create Drawings tab in the Today window, select Wizards in the Select How to Begin list.

3 On the Create Drawings tab, choose Quick Setup.

The Quick Setup wizard is displayed.

Setting the Unit Type

One of your first tasks is to select the type of unit you want to use for drawing: decimal, engineering, architectural, scientific, or fractional units. In this exercise, you choose Decimal. Coordinates and distances will be displayed in decimal rather than fractional, scientific, or other notation styles.

To set unit type

■ In the Quick Setup wizard under Select the Unit of Measurement, select Decimal. Then choose Next.

Specifying Limits

Now set your drawing boundaries. In AutoCAD LT, you can set drawing boundaries using a grid. The grid can represent the drawing area. Setting the limits helps you conceptualize the full-scale size of the objects you will draw in this tutorial. Actually, you can draw beyond the grid limits or change them at will.

Limits can be set to represent any size. For example, if you want to draw a 35 × 25 hinge block, you set your limits to be at least 50 × 40. The limits would include the 35 × 25 hinge block plus an invisible margin around it. Limits are always specified by two points, a lower-left and an upper-right.

Coordinate values are a set of numbers that specifies a point location in relation to two axes set on a flat two-dimensional (2D) surface, or drawing plane. In 2D drawing, you can specify a coordinate location with two numbers separated by a comma, such as 8,5. The first number represents the X value of the coordinate, which specifies horizontal distance from the origin (0,0). The second number represents the Y value, which specifies vertical distance.

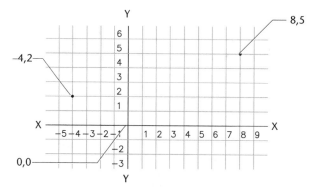

The two axes meet at the *origin* point (0,0). In the following exercise, the origin point has been automatically established for you with the Quick Setup wizard. The lower-left limit of the grid is 0,0 by default. By entering **12,9** for the upper-right corner, you establish the opposite corner of your grid limits. For more information about using coordinates, see page 112.

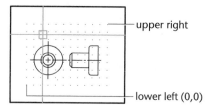

To specify limits

Specifying the drawing limits creates the user-defined rectangular boundary of the drawing area that is covered by dots when the grid is turned on. If you are using the English system of measurement, AutoCAD LT sets 12,9 as the upper-right limit of the grid by default, which is the correct setting for this exercise. If you are using the Metric system of measurement, AutoCAD LT sets 420,297 by default.

- Enter **12** in the Width box and **9** in the Length box and choose Finish to exit the wizard.

These limits can be changed at any time using the LIMITS command.

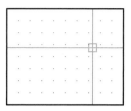

Grid turned on

Setting the Grid and Snap

Grid and snap are tools that help you draw and align your objects. Grid displays a pattern of vertical and horizontal dots on your screen. These dots are a visual aid only and are not printed. Snap restricts the movement of your pointing device so that locating points precisely is easier.

You can set grid and snap to specific values. For example, setting grid to 1 displays a pattern of dots one unit apart. Setting snap to 0.50 restricts movement of the crosshairs to every 0.50 units, or half the grid spacing. Note that the grid display is limited by the limits values.

In the following exercise, you set the snap and grid values.

To set grid and snap

1   From the Tools menu, choose Drafting Settings.

2   On the Snap and Grid tab in the Drafting Settings dialog box, select Snap On and Grid On.

    After grid and snap are turned on, enter values for *X* spacing and *Y* spacing.

3   Under Snap, enter **0.2500** next to Snap X Spacing.

4   Under Grid, enter **0.5000** next to Grid X Spacing.

    Y spacing changes automatically to match *X* spacing.

5   Choose OK.

As you move your pointing device, notice that the cursor "snaps" to an evenly spaced pattern of points between the dots, or one-half the grid spacing.

Setting Unit Precision

Next, set unit precision, which controls the number of decimal places displayed. For example, a mechanical drawing might require a high degree of precision for the bore hole on a metal plate. By default, AutoCAD LT sets precision to four decimal places. You will set precision to two decimal places.

NOTE The precision setting affects only the display of values. The internal precision is always at the highest level that can be stored with the drawing.

To set the unit precision

1 From the Format menu, choose Units.

2 In the Drawing Units dialog box, under Length, click the down arrow in the Precision box.

3 Select a two-place (0.00) decimal precision.

4 Choose OK.

Setting Ortho

Ortho mode restricts the cursor to horizontal and vertical movement. It operates within drawing and editing commands. Ortho makes it easier for you to draw straight horizontal and vertical lines. For this exercise, turn on Ortho.

To set Ortho

- On the status bar, click Ortho.

The Ortho button should appear to be indented.

Loading Linetypes

You need a continuous line, a centerline, and a dashed or hidden line to draw the bracket in this tutorial. New drawings save file space and loading time by loading only the CONTINUOUS linetype. You must load any other AutoCAD LT linetypes before you can use them. By loading the linetypes first, you can assign different linetypes to layers as you create them.

To load linetypes

1 From the Format menu, choose Linetype.

2 In the Linetype Manager, choose Load.

3 In the Load or Reload Linetypes dialog box, make sure the linetype file *aclt.lin* is selected.

4 Scroll the Available Linetypes list and select CENTER. Hold down the CTRL key, scroll the linetype list again, and select HIDDEN. Then choose OK.

5 Choose OK to close the Linetype Manager.

The CENTER and HIDDEN linetypes are loaded. The CONTINUOUS linetype is already loaded by default.

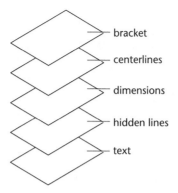

bracket

centerlines

dimensions

hidden lines

text

Sample layers

Creating Layers

Your drawing consists of many components. By creating layers, you can group various types of objects. For example, you can put objects, text, dimensions, and even title blocks on separate layers. This helps you separate plans, details, and shapes. When items such as dimensions are on a separate layer, you can turn off that layer to reduce visual clutter as you draw.

In the following exercise, you create five layers. You create a layer named Bracket for the model, Center for centerlines, Dims for dimensions, Hidden for hidden lines, and Text for annotations.

To create layers

1 From the Format menu, choose Layer.

2 In the Layer Properties Manager, choose New.

Notice that the layer you created, Layer1, now appears in the list of layers.

3 Rename this layer by typing **Bracket** on the highlighted name. Press ENTER to update the layer name.

4 Repeat steps 2 and 3 to create the following layers: Center, Dims, Hidden, and Text.

5 Choose OK.

Assigning Colors and Linetypes to Layers

When you draw manually, you use centerlines, hidden lines, and heavy or light lines to distinguish parts of your drawing. With AutoCAD LT, you can assign a specific linetype and color to each layer.

NOTE The colors available depend on your video graphics card and configuration.

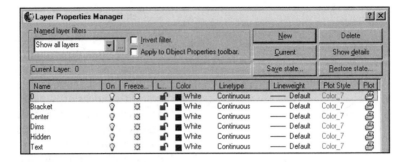

To assign colors and linetypes to layers

1 From the Format menu, choose Layer.

2 In the Layer Properties Manager, select Bracket in the Name list.

3 Under the column heading Color, click the black square.

   The Select Color dialog box displays nine standard colors and a full color palette (depending on your video graphics card).

4 In the Select Color dialog box, under Standard Colors, click the blue square. Then choose OK.

5 Change the linetype for the Center layer by clicking CONTINUOUS under the Linetype column heading.

6 In the Select Linetype dialog box, select CENTER. Then choose OK.

7 Complete assigning the colors and linetypes shown in the following table.

Layer specifications		
Layer name	Color	Linetype
Bracket	Blue	CONTINUOUS
Center	Red	CENTER
Dims	Magenta	CONTINUOUS
Hidden	Green	HIDDEN
Text	Cyan	CONTINUOUS

If you are not sure which color to choose because you don't know its hue (for example, cyan), click a standard color in the Select Color dialog box and look at the name displayed in the Color text box. Don't click OK yet.

Making a Layer Current

Once you've assigned a color and a linetype to each layer, you need to make a specific layer *current*. When a layer is current, everything you draw is drawn on that layer. You will begin drawing on the Center layer.

To make a layer current

1 In the Name list, select Center. Then choose Current.
2 Choose OK.

Saving the Drawing

By saving the drawing, you store both the drawing itself and the drawing settings, such as grid, snap, and Ortho mode, loaded linetypes, and layer names. Be sure to save your drawing frequently to avoid losing work in the event of a power failure or other unexpected event.

It is good practice to save your drawing files in a different directory or folder than the one in which you installed AutoCAD LT. For instance, you might create a folder called *project*, in which you store all your drawings for a project you're working on. In this exercise, you will save the drawing and its settings as *bracket.dwg*.

To save a drawing

1 From the File menu, choose Save.
2 In the Save Drawing As dialog box, under File Name, enter **bracket**. Remember to check which folder you are saving your file in so that you can easily find it later. Then choose Save.

You are now ready to start drawing.

Creating and Editing Objects at Full Size

When drawing with AutoCAD LT you draw at full size (1:1 scale). That is, every unit in AutoCAD LT represents one full-scale unit. You will draw the bracket at full size. This part of the tutorial takes about one hour to complete.

Drawing the Top View

You start by drawing lines and circles to create the top view. The drawing starts to take shape when you copy the lines and circles and round off the corners. You use object snaps to maintain accuracy. First, create two lines on the Center layer. These lines are used to place the circles.

To draw the vertical centerline

1 From the Draw menu, choose Line.

2 Use your pointing device to specify a point near the top of your screen. (Refer to the following illustration for placement.)

3 Drag your cursor down to the third grid dot from the bottom of the graphics area and click to place the endpoint of the line.

4 Press ENTER to end the LINE command.

NOTE Notice that you can move the cursor only horizontally or vertically. Turning Ortho on restricts cursor movement to help you draw quickly.

Now, draw a horizontal line to finish the centerlines.

To draw the horizontal centerline

1 Press ENTER to repeat the LINE command.

2 Click left of the vertical line and one quarter of the way down, or approximately at the sixth grid dot from the top of the graphics area (based on 0.5000 grid setting).

3 Drag your cursor horizontally across the graphics area and click to place the endpoint of the line.

4 Press ENTER to complete the LINE command.

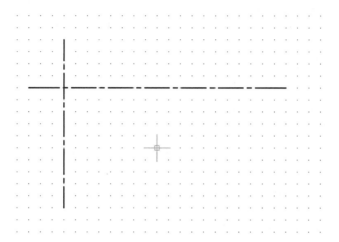

You can save time by drawing an object once and then copying it to other locations. Using an offset creates copies of an object a specified distance and direction from the original object.

In the following exercise, you use the OFFSET command to copy the vertical line 3.94 units away from the original line.

To offset the vertical line

1 From the Modify menu, choose Offset.

2 On the command line, type **3.94** for the offset distance. Then press ENTER.

Notice that the cursor changes from crosshairs to a square, called a *pickbox*. With the pickbox, you select the objects you want to copy, rotate, edit, and so on.

3 Select the vertical centerline.

4 Specify any point on the right side of the line.

5 Press ENTER to complete the command.

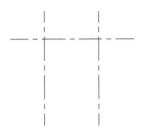

 NOTE If you make a mistake while drawing the lines, choose Undo on the toolbar. (You can also enter **u** for UNDO on the command line.)

 If you need to bring back the objects that UNDO removed, choose Redo on the toolbar. (You can also enter **redo** on the command line.)

Now that you have drawn all the centerlines, you can draw the bracket. Before you start, you need to make the Bracket layer current. This places the next objects you draw on the Bracket layer.

To make a different layer current

1 On the Object Properties toolbar, click the Layer Control arrow.

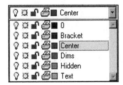

A list of layers is displayed.

2 Select the layer called Bracket.

To begin drawing the top view of the object, you draw two circles.

Object snaps help you draw with precision. For example, to draw a line from the center point of an existing circle, use the Center object snap. When you click the edge of the circle, the cursor snaps to the center point of the circle as the start point of the line.

In this exercise you draw a circle by specifying its center and radius, using the Intersection object snap to specify a center point.

To draw the large circle

1 From the Draw menu, choose Circle ➤ Center, Radius.

2 To display the object snap menu, press SHIFT and right-click. Then choose Intersection.

Notice that the crosshairs change to an X as you move the cursor over the intersection of the centerlines.

3 Click near the intersection of the centerlines on the left to specify the center of the circle.

Although the centerlines are on a different layer, you can still use them as snap points when drawing on the Bracket layer.

4 On the command line, enter **1.5** for the radius.

5 Press ENTER to complete the circle.

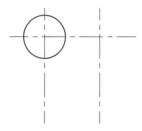

To draw the small circle

1 Press ENTER to restart the CIRCLE command.

2 From the object snap menu, choose Intersection.

3 Click near the intersection of the centerlines on the right to specify the center of the circle.

4 On the command line, enter **.55** for the radius.

5 Press ENTER to complete the circle.

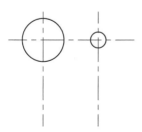

Save your drawing.

You just used single object snaps for precision drawing. You can set *running* objects snaps so AutoCAD LT identifies specific object snaps automatically every time your pointing device moves over a snap point in your drawing. For the purposes of this exercise, you will set running object snaps for Endpoint, Center, and Quadrant.

To set running object snaps

1 From the Tools menu, choose Drafting Settings.

2 On the Object Snap tab in the Drafting Settings dialog box, make sure that Object Snap On is selected. Under Object Snap Modes, select the boxes next to Endpoint, Center, and Quadrant.

3 Choose OK.

Having created the circles, you can now start on the lines. You can draw one line, and then copy it to another location. The next procedure helps you practice using object snaps and teaches you how to copy an object.

To draw the top line

1 From the Draw menu, choose Line.

2 Move the cursor near the top of the larger circle to specify the top quadrant point of the circle. The Quadrant AutoSnap marker should be displayed at the circle's quadrant. If not, press the TAB key to cycle through the object snap candidates until the quadrant marker is displayed. Click to specify the first point of the line. Notice that the AutoSnap magnet automatically locates the circle's quadrant; AutoCAD LT does the precision work for you.

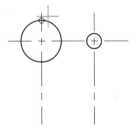

Quadrant AutoSnap marker
displayed at the circle's top quadrant

3 Move the pointing device to draw a line about the same length as the horizontal centerline, and then click to specify the endpoint of the line.

4 Press ENTER to complete the line.

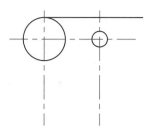

Next, copy the line at the lowest point of the circle. Use the Quadrant object snap for precise placement.

To copy a line

1 From the Modify menu, choose Copy.

2 Click the line above the circle to select it.

3 Press ENTER to complete object selection.

4 For a base point, select the top quadrant of the large circle. Move the cursor near the top of the larger circle to specify the top quadrant point of the circle. The Quadrant AutoSnap marker should be displayed at the circle's quadrant. If not, press TAB to cycle through the object snap candidates until the Quadrant marker is displayed. Click to specify the base point.

5 For the displacement point, select the bottom quadrant of the large circle. The Quadrant AutoSnap marker is displayed at the circle's quadrant. Click to specify the displacement point.

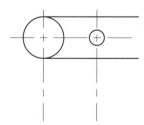

Finishing the Top View

A few steps remain to finish the top view. First, you will round off the corners of the bracket by using the FILLET command, which connects two objects with a smooth arc. Then you draw an eight-sided hole inside the larger circle.

To draw a vertical line

1 From the Draw menu, choose Line.

2 To begin the line at the right quadrant of the small circle, move the cursor near the right side of the small circle to specify the right quadrant point of the circle. The Quadrant AutoSnap marker is displayed at the circle's quadrant. Click to specify the right quadrant.

3 Move the cursor down and click for the endpoint of the line. Use the line length in the following illustration as a guide.

4 Press ENTER to complete the line.

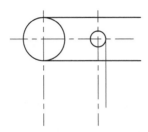

Next you will offset the line at a distance of one unit from the original line.

To offset the vertical line

1 From the Modify menu, choose Offset.

2 On the command line, enter **1** for the offset distance. Then press ENTER.

3 Select the vertical line on the small circle.

4 Click to the right of the line.

5 Press ENTER to complete the command.

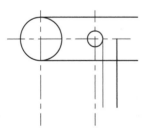

With two lines to work with, you can create a *fillet* to round off the corners of your bracket. In drafting terms, an outside curve is a *round*, and an inside curve is a fillet. In AutoCAD LT, both are created with the FILLET command.

Before FILLET   **After FILLET**

Before you can create a fillet, you set the radius of its arc. The value for a radius can be from 0 to an unlimited value restricted only by the size of your object. A fillet with a 0 radius is equivalent to a square corner. Any other value rounds the corners. In this procedure, you round off the corners of the bracket using a fillet with a radius of 0.50.

To set the fillet radius and fillet two lines

1 From the Modify menu, choose Fillet.

2 On the command line, enter **r** (Radius). Then press ENTER.

3 Enter **.5** for the radius of the fillet. (Because this value is the default for the radius, you may not have to enter anything.) Then press ENTER.

   Now you need to select the objects that you want to fillet.

4 Select the offset vertical line on the right (1).

5 Select the line at the top of the large circle (2).

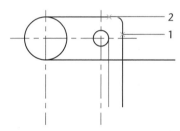

6 Press ENTER to repeat the FILLET command.

7 Repeat steps 4 and 5 to create another fillet for the line at the bottom of the larger circle.

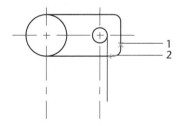

Now create an eight-sided hole inside the larger circle by drawing a polygon with a radius of 0.61. Use the Center object snap in this exercise.

To draw a polygon

1 From the Draw menu, choose Polygon.

2 On the command line, enter **8** to specify the number of sides.

3 Move the cursor near the center of the larger circle to snap to the center of the circle. Press TAB to cycle through the available object snaps until the Center marker is displayed at the circle's center. Click to specify the center point.

4 Enter **c** on the command line to draw a polygon that circumscribes a circle of the radius you specify.

5 On the command line, enter **.61** for the radius of the circle whose circumference is tangent to the polygon segments.

Save your drawing.

Now that you have finished part of the top view, you may notice that there's an unnecessary line on the right of the smaller circle (1). You can use the ERASE command to delete unwanted objects. In this exercise, you will use a shortcut menu to delete the unneeded line.

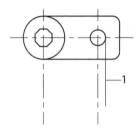

To erase an object

1 Select the vertical line at the right quadrant of the small circle to activate its grips.

2 Right-click in the graphics area to display the shortcut menu. Choose Erase or Cut to delete the line.

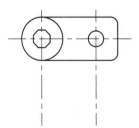

Exiting AutoCAD LT

If you want to do the rest of the tutorial later, exit the program.

To exit AutoCAD LT

■ From the File menu, choose Exit.

If you have not saved your most recent changes, choose Yes when the dialog box is displayed.

Opening an Existing Drawing

When you open a drawing, AutoCAD LT loads all the drawing settings that you set before the file was saved.

To start AutoCAD LT

1 From the Start menu, choose Programs ➤ AutoCAD LT 2000i. Then choose AutoCAD LT 2000i.

2 On the Open Drawings tab in the Today window, select Most Recently Used in the Select How to Begin list.

A list of drawing files is displayed.

3 If the file you are looking for is displayed in the list, select it and skip the remaining step of this procedure. Otherwise, choose Browse.

4 In the Open dialog box, find the folder in which you created the drawing. Select *bracket.dwg* from the list of files. Then choose Open.

Drawing the Front View

You can use the top-view drawing as a guide to draw the front view of the bracket. You use the LINE and OFFSET commands, as well as the TRIM command, to complete the front view.

In this exercise, you start by drawing some lines near the bottom of the screen.

To draw a horizontal line

1 From the Draw menu, choose Line.

2 Click approximately one quarter of the way up from the bottom of the screen, near the left edge of the graphics area (1), using the start point of the horizontal centerline as a guide.

3 Move your cursor horizontally from the left side of the screen to the right. Click to the right of the edge of the bracket for the endpoint of the line (2), as shown in the illustration.

NOTE If the cursor is not constrained to vertical and horizontal movements, click Ortho on the status bar to turn it on.

---

4 Press ENTER to complete the command.

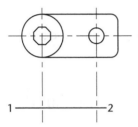

If necessary, you can adjust the length of the line later.

Next, you need to offset the line for the top portion of the front view of the bracket.

To offset a line

1 From the Modify menu, choose Offset.

2 On the command line, enter **1.97** for the offset distance and press ENTER.

3 Select the horizontal line at the bottom of the screen.

4 Click anywhere above the line.

5 Press ENTER to complete the command.

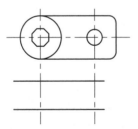

Now you should have two lines, as shown in the illustration. To create the middle line, use OFFSET again to copy the line from the bottom of the front view.

To offset a line

1 Press ENTER to repeat the OFFSET command.
2 On the command line, enter **.79** for the offset distance.
3 Select the same horizontal line at the bottom of the screen.
4 Click anywhere above the line.
5 Press ENTER to complete the command.

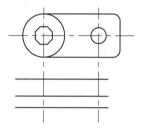

Now that you have baselines for the front view of the bracket, you can draw construction lines from the top view to the front view. These lines help you align the top view with the front view. Using the Quadrant and Endpoint object snaps, you will draw the lines to complete the figure.

To draw the left vertical line from the large circle

1 From the Draw menu, choose Line.
2 Move your pointing device near the left side of the larger circle to specify the left quadrant. The Quadrant marker is displayed at the circle's quadrant. Click to specify the first point of the line.
3 Drag your cursor down vertically and draw a line approximately the same length as the vertical centerlines. Click to specify the endpoint of the line.
4 Press ENTER to complete the line.

To draw the right vertical line from the large circle

1 Right-click in the graphics area to display the shortcut menu. Choose Repeat Line to repeat the LINE command.
2 Move your pointing device near the right side of the larger circle. The Quadrant AutoSnap marker is displayed at the circle's right quadrant. Click to specify the start point of the line.
3 Drag your cursor down vertically and draw a line approximately the same length as the vertical centerlines. Click to specify the endpoint of the line.
4 Press ENTER to complete the line.

To draw the right end of the bracket

1 Press ENTER to repeat the LINE command.

2 Move the cursor near the lower endpoint of the right vertical edge of the top view (point 1 in the following illustration). The Endpoint AutoSnap marker is displayed at the line's endpoint. Click to specify the start point of the line you are drawing.

3 Drag your cursor down vertically and draw a line approximately the same length as the vertical centerlines. Click to specify the endpoint of the line.

4 Press ENTER to complete the line.

Before
EXTEND

Now that you have drawn the vertical ends of the bracket, notice that the horizontal lines do not overlap or touch the right vertical end line. The EXTEND command extends objects such as lines and arcs to other objects that you define as boundary edges.

After
EXTEND

In this exercise, you extend the bottom and the middle horizontal lines to the right vertical end line of the bracket.

You might find it easier to select the lines with Snap turned off.

To turn Snap off

■ On the status bar, click Snap.

To extend the horizontal lines

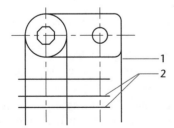

1 From the Modify menu, choose Extend.

2 Select the vertical line at the right end of the bracket as the boundary edge (1). Then press ENTER.

3 Click near the right end of the bottom and the middle horizontal lines to select the objects to extend (2).

4 Press ENTER to end the command.

Now that all the lines overlap or touch one another, you can trim or cut the lines to create the outline of the front view. Using TRIM removes portions of lines.

To trim lines where they intersect

1 From the Modify menu, choose Trim.

2 Select the top (1) and bottom (2) lines of the front view as the cutting edges. Then press ENTER to complete the object selection set.

3 Select the lines (3 and 4) as shown in the illustration for the objects to trim.

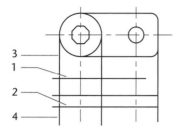

If you make a mistake, choose Undo on the toolbar.

4 Press ENTER to end the command.

Your drawing should look like the following illustration.

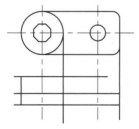

5 Use TRIM to remove the rest of the lines to complete the figure as shown in the following illustration.

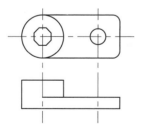

To represent the holes in the plan view, you draw hidden lines. First, you'll need to make Hidden the current layer.

To make a new layer current

1 On the Object Properties toolbar, click the Layer Control arrow.

2 From the layer list, select Hidden.

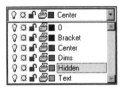

Next, you will draw lines from the polygon and the small circle to represent the holes in the front view, as shown in the following illustration.

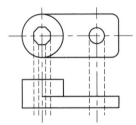

To draw the hidden lines from the polygon

1 From the Draw menu, choose Line.

2 Move the cursor near the right edge of the polygon in the top view of the bracket. The Endpoint AutoSnap marker is displayed at the edge's lower endpoint. Click to specify the start point of the line you are drawing.

3 Move the cursor down vertically. Then click to locate the endpoint of the line.

4 Press ENTER to complete the line.

5 Draw the remaining vertical lines from the edges of the polygon by repeating steps 1 through 4.

If you have trouble completing the lines in step 4, click Osnap on the status bar to temporarily turn off running object snaps and complete the line. You can click Osnap again to turn on object snaps before you start the next line.

Now draw lines from the small circle.

To draw the hidden lines from the small circle

1 From the Draw menu, choose Line.

2 Move the cursor near the right quadrant of the small circle. When the Quadrant AutoSnap marker is displayed, click to specify the start point of the line you are drawing.

3 Move the cursor down vertically. Then click to locate the endpoint of the line.

4 Press ENTER to complete the line.

5 Draw the left vertical line from the left quadrant of the small circle by repeating steps 1 through 4. Select the left side of the circle to start your line.

Next, using TRIM, remove the unwanted portions of the lines.

To trim lines where they intersect

1 From the Modify menu, select Trim.

2 Select the top and bottom lines of the front view as the cutting edges (1, 2, and 3), as shown in the illustration. Press ENTER to complete the object selection set.

3 Select the hidden line on the left in two places (4 and 5).

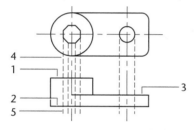

4 Select the rest of the hidden lines to complete the figure as shown in the following illustration.

5 Press ENTER to end the command.

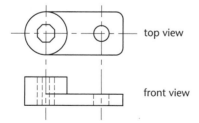

top view

front view

Save your drawing.

Now that you've completed the top and front views, you are ready to dimension your drawing.

Dimensioning the Drawing

With the help of object snaps, you can dimension your drawing. This part of the tutorial takes about 30 minutes to complete.

By placing all your dimensions on the Dims layer, you can separate them from the objects you have drawn. Separating your dimensions gives you more precise control over their appearance. The dimensions for this drawing consist of horizontal, vertical, radius, and diameter dimensions.

To make the Dims layer current

1 On the Object Properties toolbar, click the Layer Control arrow.

2 From the layer list, select Dims.

Before you add dimensions to the drawing, you can change the dimension style to suit your needs. In this procedure, you change the default precision.

To change the default dimension style

1 From the Format menu, choose Dimension Style.

2 In the Dimension Style Manager, choose Override.

3 In the Override Current Style dialog box, Primary Units tab, under Linear Dimensions, select 0.00 as the precision.

4 Choose OK and then Close to exit each dialog box.

You will dimension the top view using linear dimensioning. Use object snaps to specify the first and second extension line origins.

To create a linear horizontal dimension

1 From the Dimension menu, choose Linear.

2 Move the cursor to the intersection of the left vertical centerline and the lower quadrant of the large circle (1) to specify the first extension line origin. The Quadrant AutoSnap marker is displayed at the lower quadrant of the large circle. Click to specify the first extension line origin. Refer to the following illustration.

3 Move the cursor to a point near the intersection of the other vertical centerline and the lower quadrant of the small circle (2) to specify the second extension line origin. The Quadrant AutoSnap marker is displayed at the lower quadrant of the small circle. Click to specify the second extension line origin.

4 Using your pointing device, specify a location for the horizontal dimension (3).

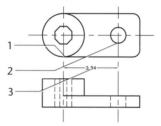

The extension lines may not be visible, because they coincide with the centerlines.

NOTE If you are using metric units, your dimensions may not look exactly like the ones in the illustrations.

You use linear dimensioning and object snaps to create the next vertical dimension.

To create a linear vertical dimension

1 From the Dimension menu, choose Linear.

2 In the top view, move the cursor near the top quadrant of the large circle to specify the first extension line origin (1). The Quadrant AutoSnap marker is displayed at the circle's quadrant. Click to specify the first extension line origin.

3 Move the cursor near the bottom quadrant of the large circle to specify the second extension line origin (2). The Quadrant AutoSnap marker is displayed at the circle's quadrant. Click to specify the second extension line origin.

4 Using your pointing device, specify a location for the vertical dimension (3).

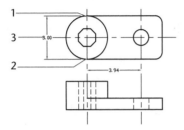

Save your drawing.

To dimension the fillet on the top view, use radial dimensioning, which includes radius and diameter dimensions. Radius dimensions automatically place an *R* symbol in front of the dimension text.

To create a radius dimension

1 From the Dimension menu, choose Radius.

2 In the plan (top) view, select one of the fillets.

3 Using your pointing device, specify a location for placement of the radius dimension.

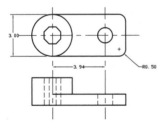

Next, you dimension the small circle in the top view using a diameter dimension. Diameter dimensions automatically place a ∅ symbol in front of the dimension text.

To create a diameter dimension

1 From the Dimension menu, choose Diameter.

2 Select the smaller circle.

3 Using your pointing device, specify a location for the diameter dimension.

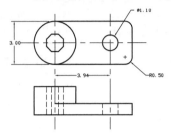

4 Using linear dimensioning, continue to dimension the top and front view as shown in the following illustration.

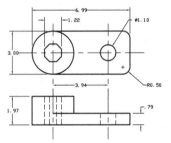

For the 0.79 linear dimension at the lower-right corner, select the endpoint at the bottom of the vertical line first, and then select the top of the vertical line.

NOTE Depending on your dimension style settings, your dimensions may not look exactly like the ones in the illustrations.

Adding Annotation

When you add annotations you can enter a single line or multiple lines of text and see the text on the screen as you enter it. A variety of text fonts are available, and each text font can be assigned to a specific text style. In this exercise, you will use the default text style and font. Before starting, set the current layer to Text to ensure that all annotations are placed on the correct layer.

This part of the tutorial takes approximately 5 minutes to complete.

To make a layer current

■ On the Object Properties toolbar, select Text in the Layer Control.

Next, you can create several lines of text.

To create multiple lines of text

1 From the Draw menu, choose Text ➤ Multiline Text.

2 Specify a point near the lower-right corner of your drawing area.

   This is the start point for a boundary that defines the width of the paragraph of text.

   Move the cursor down and to the right and then click to specify the right-hand limit of the bounding box.

   The Multiline Text Editor is displayed.

3 Enter *Your Company Name* and press ENTER to start a new line.

4 Enter **BY:** *Your Name* and press ENTER.

5 Choose OK.

Notice that the text wraps so it fits in the bounding box you specified.

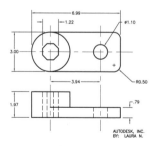

Save your drawing.

Plotting the Drawing

You are now ready to print or plot your drawing on paper. Although there are more advanced methods of layout and printing available for complex drawings, these methods are not necessary for a simple 2D drawing such as this one.

This part of the tutorial takes approximately 10 minutes to complete.

Before you start, you will need to make sure the printer or plotter is turned on and the correct size paper is set for use. If you are using a pen plotter, check to see that the pens are working and are secure in the pen holder.

To select a printer or plotter

1 From the File menu, choose Plot.

   The Plot dialog box is displayed. If you have more than one printer or plotter available, you need to set which printer or plotter you want to use.

2 On the Plot Device tab, under Plotter Configuration, select the printer or plotter you want to use from the list next to Name.

Once you have selected the printer or plotter, you need to select the paper size and orientation. Your Windows default system printer is the default printer for AutoCAD LT.

To select a paper size and orientation

1 In the Plot dialog box, choose the Plot Settings tab.

2 Under Paper Size and Units, select the size of the paper that is currently loaded in your printer or plotter.

3 Under Drawing Orientation, select Portrait.

Having selected the paper size and orientation, you can select the area you want to be printed or plotted. In the following exercise, you will use the drawing extents as your plotting area. In this exercise, the drawing extents represents the area covered by the grid limits.

To set the plot area

■ On the Plot Settings tab, under Plot Area, select Extents.

Once the plotting area is established, you can set the plotting scale. Although you've drawn the objects at their full size, you can plot the drawing either to a specific scale or to fit the paper size.

You are going to plot this drawing at 1:2, that is, half scale.

To set the plotting scale

- In the Plot dialog box, under Plot Scale, select 1:2 from the list next to Scale.

You can save time and paper by previewing the plot before it is printed. There are two preview options: Partial and Full. Partial Preview shows an outline representation of the plotting area in relation to the paper size. Full Preview displays the drawing as it will be plotted on the paper.

To preview a drawing

1 In the Plot dialog box, choose Full Preview.
2 In the preview image, right-click to display the shortcut menu, and choose Exit.

   The drawing is displayed as it will look when plotted.

NOTE You will probably need to make some adjustments to fit the drawing properly on the paper. You can change the paper orientation to Landscape or set the plotting scale to another value. If the drawing was not centered on the paper, you can select Center the Plot under Plot Offset. Or, you can adjust the *X* and *Y* values under Plot Offset to center the image. Once you have made adjustments, do another plot preview. When you have set the correct plotting scale and previewed the drawing, you are ready to plot your drawing.

To send the drawing to the printer or plotter

- In the Plot dialog box, choose OK.

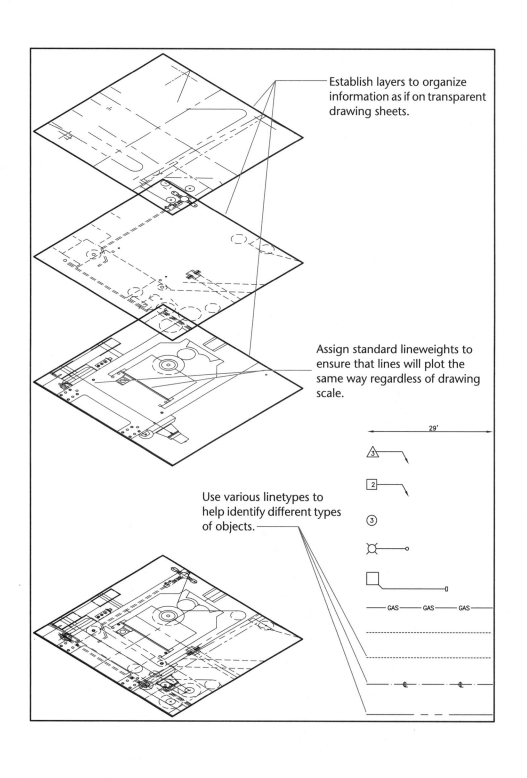

Establish layers to organize information as if on transparent drawing sheets.

Assign standard lineweights to ensure that lines will plot the same way regardless of drawing scale.

Use various linetypes to help identify different types of objects.

Drawing Setup

5

Starting a computer-based drawing differs fundamentally from using a paper-based approach. With CAD, you don't have to plan scaling and layout in detail before you start drawing. You should do some planning, however. This chapter helps you begin.

The AutoCAD LT® window provides two parallel working environments—represented by the Model tab and the Layout tabs. You should have some ideas about how you will lay out and scale your drawing before you start work because this affects the way you create and scale dimensions, lines, and text. You should also plan drawing layers so you can organize drawing information and use the same linetypes and colors for related items. You can also set AutoCAD LT options and create standard templates that help you work efficiently.

In this chapter

- Starting a Drawing
- Planning Drawing Units and Scale
- Understanding Models and Layouts
- Planning Dimension, Linetype, and Text Scales
- Organizing Drawings with Layers, Lines, and Colors
- Setting AutoCAD LT Options

Starting a Drawing

When you create a new drawing in AutoCAD LT, start with the AutoCAD LT Today window or the Create New Drawing dialog box, which provide three setup options:

- *Use a Wizard* offers Quick Setup and Advanced Setup wizards.
- *Start from Scratch* requires minimal setup information.
- *Use a Template* opens a file with a previously saved setup.

Using a Wizard

Using a wizard is an easy way to start a new drawing. The Quick Setup and Advanced Setup wizards are described below.

Both the Quick Setup wizard and Advanced Setup wizard specify these items:

- *Units*. The type of unit of measurement (Decimal, Engineering, Architectural, Fractional, or Scientific) and *precision* (the number of decimal places or fractional settings you need to see displayed)
- *Area*. The *limits* of the grid, often used to denote the drawing area

The Quick Setup wizard accepts the defaults for Angle (Decimal Degrees), Angle Measure (East), and Angle Direction (Counterclockwise). To specify new values for these settings, use the Advanced Setup wizard.

- *Angle*. The unit type with which angles are measured (Decimal Degrees, Degrees/Minutes/Seconds, Grads, Radians, or Surveyor)
- *Angle Measure*. The start point for angle measurement (East, North, West, South, Other)
- *Angle Direction*. The direction in which angles are measured (Counterclockwise or Clockwise)

Starting from Scratch

When you choose to start a new drawing from scratch, you must specify the type of unit of measurement you will use. For this option, AutoCAD LT supplies default template drawing files for English (feet and inches) and for Metric measurement settings. You can specify all other drawing parameters using the menus and the command line.

Using a Template

A *template drawing* file contains standard settings; you can use any drawing as a template drawing. When you use an existing drawing as a template, all information is passed on to the new drawing. You create an AutoCAD LT drawing template file by saving a drawing using the *.dwt* extension.

You can save time by preparing some standard templates. Include settings and basic drawing elements that you will use often, such as

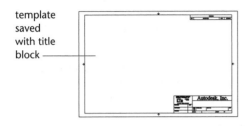

template saved with title block

- Unit type and precision
- Drawing grid limits
- Snap, grid, and Ortho settings
- Layer organization
- Title blocks, borders, and logos
- Dimension and text styles
- Linetypes, lineweights, and plot styles

NOTE You can import layouts from drawing template files into open drawings. For information about layouts, see page 100.

To get started		
Action	**Menu**	**Toolbar**
Creating a new drawing	File ➤ New Tools ➤ Today	Standard Internet
Creating a template	File ➤ Save As	Standard

ONLINE HELP NEW, TODAY, Scratch, Template, Wizard

Planning Drawing Units and Scale

In AutoCAD LT, you don't need to worry about setting a scale before you start drawing. Even though you eventually print or plot to paper, the *model* you draw on screen doesn't have to fit a particular sheet size. However, your planning must include determining an appropriate value for AutoCAD LT drawing units so you can easily display your model on a *layout*.

Drawing units represent whatever you want them to on the screen. At drawing setup, you designate the type of on-screen units of measurement— decimal, engineering, architectural, fractional, or scientific. For example, one unit can equal one inch, one foot, one centimeter, one meter, or one mile. Next, you indicate the estimated size of your model by setting the drawing grid limits, which you can easily exceed or change. Then you draw in virtual *full size* based on the units you identified. A *grid* pattern can provide a visible representation of drawing units and limits on the screen.

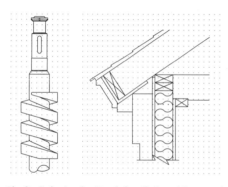

Shaft, 1 decimal unit = 1cm   **Roof detail, 1 architectural unit = 1 inch**   **Office plan, 1 architectural unit = 1 foot**

You can zoom in or out to change the apparent size of the model. The scale of the drawing matters only when you transfer it to paper, using one of these methods for creating hard copies:

- ***Printing or plotting from the model.*** In this case, you handle scaling when you produce the hard copy. When you print or plot, you specify a scale so the drawing on the screen fits exactly on the drawing sheet.
- ***Printing or plotting from a layout.*** In this case, you set up a page layout on the screen and scale the model using the ZOOM command before you plot. In the layout, you arrange one or more views of your drawing on the on-screen drawing sheet. You can use a different scale for each view and then plot the sheet at 1:1 scale.

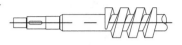

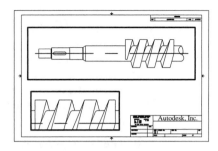

Drawing model

**Drawing layout with title block and
border inserted**

Scaling drawings for plotting affects the appearance of text, dimensions, and
lines. For more information, see page 102.

To get started		
Action	Menu	Toolbar
Setting units and limits	File ➤ New	Standard
Scaling in model space	File ➤ Print	Standard
Scaling in layout viewports	File ➤ Zoom	Standard/Viewports

ONLINE HELP UNITS, LIMITS, NEW, PLOT, ZOOM

Understanding Models and Layouts

The AutoCAD LT window provides two parallel working environments represented by the Model and Layout tabs. Working on the Model tab, you draw a model of your subject. On the Layout tabs, you can arrange multiple "snapshots" of the model. Each layout represents a drawing sheet that can display one or more views of the model at various scales.

- **The Model tab accesses a limitless drawing area.** In *model space*, you draw at 1:1 scale, and you decide whether one unit represents one inch (for a bracket) or one meter (for a bridge).
- **Layout tabs access virtual drawing sheets.** When you set up a layout, you tell AutoCAD LT the sheet size you want to use. The layout represents the drawing sheet. This layout environment is called *paper space*.

Drawing in Model Space

To create a model of the subject you want to represent, select the Model tab. Then draw your subject matter using the precision drawing tools.

If you don't require a complex layout, you can plot directly from model space. If you intend to do this—or to add dimensions, a title block, or text to the model space drawing—you must do a little planning. You must size text, dimensions, and title blocks inserted in the model space drawing so they appear correctly proportioned when you scale the drawing for printing or plotting.

Working in Layouts

To create a layout, select a Layout tab. AutoCAD LT displays a virtual drawing sheet where you can arrange views of your model. Here you create viewports that act as windows into model space—each viewport can contain a different view. For more information about using viewports, see page 130.

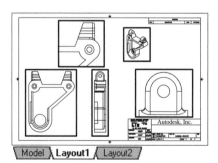

Layout with viewports using different scales

When you add a title block, text, or dimensions to a layout, you create them at true size, the size they will be when plotted.

You can create numerous layouts for a single drawing file. For each layout you create, you can specify plotter, sheet size, and the title block to include in the Page Setup dialog box. You can specify basic information in the Page Setup dialog box when you create the layout and then add other information later—for example, when you print or plot the drawing. For more information about plotting from a layout, see page 264.

To get started		
Action	**Menu**	**Tab**
Drawing in model space		Model
Creating layouts	File ➤ Page Setup	Layout1, Layout2, etc.

ONLINE HELP MODEL, LAYOUT

Planning Dimension, Linetype, and Text Scales

The arrangement of a drawing on paper is an important part of the drawing process. Preparing multiple views of a drawing usually involves displaying them at various scales. So, you must plan dimensions, linetypes, and text to make sure they appear at the right size.

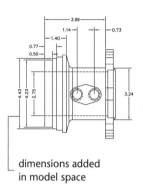

dimensions added
in model space

Scaling Dimensions and Text in Model Space

You can add dimensions and text—even a title block—to your drawing while working in model space. Remember, however, that you will probably scale your model later for printing or plotting. Therefore, you must estimate the size you want for text and dimensions in the plotted drawing and calculate what size they have to be in model space to look appropriate when plotted. You then set up your text styles and dimension styles accordingly. For more information, see page 200 regarding text styles and page 216 regarding dimension styles.

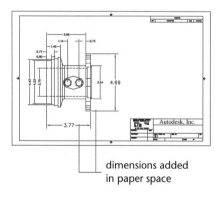

dimensions added
in paper space

Scaling Dimensions and Text in a Layout

If you add dimensions, title blocks, and text to a layout in paper space, you can create them at their final size. However, radial dimensions are not supported in the Layout tabs, and you must create them in model space. Dimensions created in paper space are not associative. Therefore, they are not updated automatically when you change your model. For this reason, many users create and scale all dimensions in model space.

Scaling Linetypes

When you scale multiple views of a drawing in a layout, you can create inconsistencies in the appearance of *linetypes*. Linetypes determine the way that lines are displayed. In noncontinuous linetypes, the length of dashes and dots, and the space between them, may grow or shrink. You can control the scaling to correspond to the model or layout scale or to remain the same at any zoom scale.

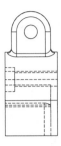

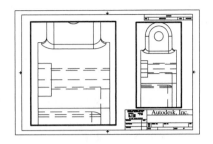

**Dashed linetype
scaled to the model**

**Dashed linetype
scaled to the layout**

To get started	
Action	**Menu**
Scaling linetype patterns	Format ➤ Linetype

ONLINE HELP PLTSCALE, LTSCALE, CELTSCALE

Organizing Drawings with Layers, Lines, and Colors

Layers are the equivalent of the overlays used in paper-based drafting. They are an important organizational tool in AutoCAD LT.

AutoCAD LT assigns the current color, linetype, and lineweight automatically to new objects you create. If the current, color, linetype, and lineweight are set to BYLAYER (default), objects are created with the color, linetype, and lineweight assigned to the current layer.

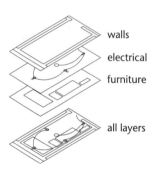

walls

electrical

furniture

all layers

Planning Layers

Whether you are drawing on the default layer (0) or a layer you create and name yourself, each layer has an associated color, linetype, and lineweight. You can organize the drawing by assigning similar components to the same layer. For example, you can create a layer for centerlines and assign the color blue and the CENTER linetype to that layer. Whenever you draw centerlines, you switch to that layer. So, every centerline object you draw is blue and uses the CENTER linetype. Later, if you don't want to display or plot centerlines, you can turn off that layer.

Controlling Layers

To make objects on a layer invisible, turn off the layer or freeze it in the Layer Properties Manager. You can also lock layers to reduce the possibility of modifying objects accidentally.

- *Turning off layers*. Use this option rather than freezing if you frequently need to switch a layer's visibility. When you turn a layer back on, the objects on the layer are displayed more quickly.
- *Freezing layers*. Use this option if you don't need a layer to be visible for a long time. Thawing a frozen layer causes an automatic regeneration of the drawing and is slower than turning a layer on.
- *Locking layers*. Use this option to prevent objects on a layer from being modified. You can still use the objects on a locked layer for operations that don't modify the objects. For example, you can snap to these objects to use them as guides for precision drawing.

Using Linetypes

───────────	CONTINUOUS
----------	HIDDEN
— - —— - —	CENTER
——— - - ——	PHANTOM

You can associate a single linetype with all of the AutoCAD LT objects drawn on the same layer. You can use linetypes to distinguish the purpose of one line from another, for example, dashed lines for hidden objects or dot-dash lines for centerlines. You can use any of the standard linetypes that AutoCAD LT provides, or you can create your own linetypes. To use a linetype, you must first load it into your drawing.

Assigning Lineweights

Lineweights add width to objects. They are independent of the current display scale. By assigning a lineweight to a layer, you ensure that objects on that layer always appear and plot at the specified width, regardless of scale.

NOTE You can assign a color, linetype, or lineweight to individual objects, regardless of layer. For more information about object properties, see page 136.

To get started

Action	Menu	Toolbar
Creating and modifying layers	Format ➤ Layer	Object Properties
Loading and managing linetypes	Format ➤ Linetype	
Changing lineweight settings	Format ➤ Lineweight	Object Properties

ONLINE HELP LAYER, LINETYPE

Setting AutoCAD LT Options

You can customize many AutoCAD LT settings in the Options dialog box. Other options are set by using system variables on the command line.

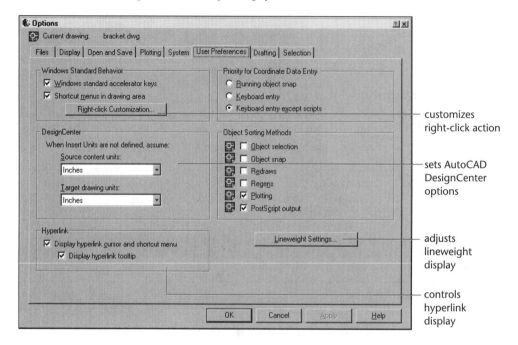

- customizes right-click action
- sets AutoCAD DesignCenter options
- adjusts lineweight display
- controls hyperlink display

- **Files tab** specifies the folders in which AutoCAD LT searches for support, driver, menu, and other files.
- **Display tab** controls display settings that affect the AutoCAD LT drawing environment and performance.
- **Open and Save tab** controls options related to opening and saving files.
- **Plotting tab** includes default plotting settings.
- **System tab** controls options for system settings and pointing devices.
- **User Preferences tab** optimizes the way you work in AutoCAD LT.
- **Drafting tab** specifies a number of general editing options.
- **Selection tab** controls settings that relate to object selection methods.

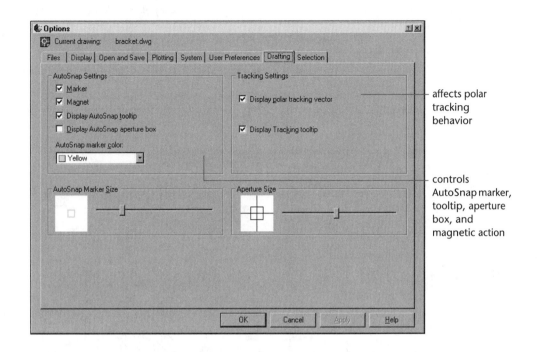

affects polar tracking behavior

controls AutoSnap marker, tooltip, aperture box, and magnetic action

To get started	
Action	**Menu**
Setting options	Tools ➤ Options

ONLINE HELP OPTIONS

Enter coordinate values to locate points precisely. ——

Turn on polar tracking to draw along specified angles. ——

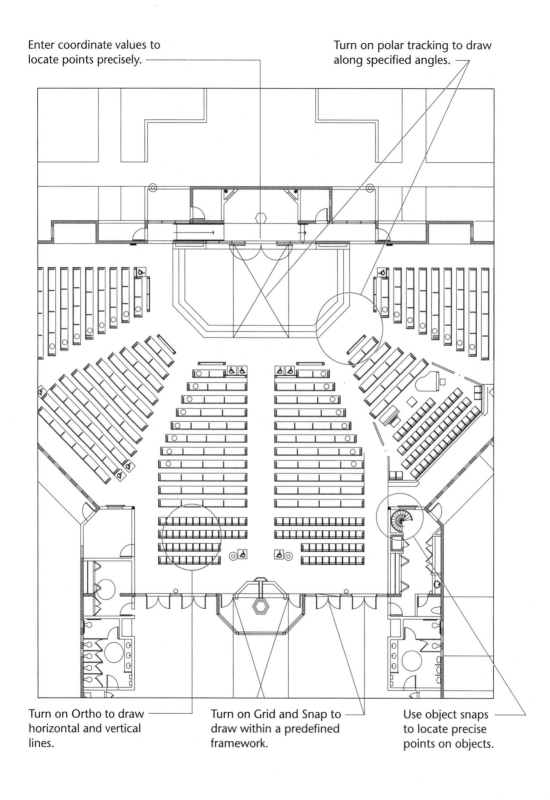

Turn on Ortho to draw horizontal and vertical lines. ——

Turn on Grid and Snap to draw within a predefined framework. ——

Use object snaps to locate precise points on objects. ——

Precision Drawing

AutoCAD LT® provides drafting settings and drawing tools to help you work with precision. Knowing you can rely on these aids also helps you draw faster. For example, displaying a drawing grid that helps you to draw within a predefined framework is similar to placing a sheet of graph paper under your drawing. The Ortho setting restricts cursor movement to the horizontal or vertical axis, as if you were using a T-square. Polar-Snap restricts cursor movement to specified angles, as if you were using a triangle. In addition, you can create objects based on precise points that you enter as Cartesian or polar coordinates. You can also snap the cursor to precise points on objects or to intervals on the screen.

In this chapter

Setting Grid and Snap Values

AutoCAD LT grid and snap features set up a framework you can use as a guide while drawing.

- *The grid* is a pattern of dots that extends over the area specified by the drawing grid limits. The grid helps you align objects and visualize the distances between them.
- *Snap* restricts the movement of the crosshairs to intervals that you have defined. When Snap is on, the cursor seems to adhere, or "snap," to an invisible grid. Snap is useful for specifying precise points with the pointing device.

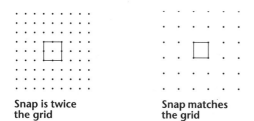

Snap is twice the grid

Snap matches the grid

Setting Grid and Snap Spacing

The grid does not necessarily correspond to the current snap interval. For example, you might set a wide grid spacing to be used as a reference but maintain a closer snap spacing for accuracy in specifying points. If you zoom in or out, you might need to adjust grid spacing to be more appropriate for the new magnification. The grid does not appear in the plotted drawing.

Turning Grid and Snap On and Off

You can turn Grid and Snap on and off at any time.

- To toggle Grid on and off, double-click Grid on the status bar, enter the GRID command, press CTRL+G, or press F7.
- To toggle Snap on and off, double-click Snap on the status bar, enter the SNAP command, press CTRL+B, or press F9.

Adjusting Snap and Grid Alignment

To draw along a specific alignment, you can change the snap and grid angle to constrain the cursor to the new alignment. For information about changing alignment in isometric drawings, see page 120.

Setting Grid Limits

When you start a new drawing, you set the rectangular boundary, or limits, of the drawing grid by using the Quick Setup or Advanced Setup wizard. You can also set, or reset, the limits when you are working on a drawing and the grid is turned on.

Grid limits shown by range of grid

The primary function of the drawing grid is to mark the area in the drawing in which you are currently working. Although you can draw beyond the limits or reset the limits at any time, the drawing grid limits can also serve as

- A drawing tool that you can use to prevent drawing outside the limits if you set the LIMCHECK system variable to 1
- A plot option that defines an area to be printed from model space

To get started		
Action	Menu	Dialog box tab
Setting Snap and Grid spacing	Tools ➤ Drafting Settings	Snap and Grid

ONLINE HELP GRID, SNAP, DSETTINGS, LIMITS, LIMCHECK

Drawing with Coordinates

Coordinate values represent a location in your drawing. When a command prompts you for a point, you can use the pointing device to specify a point in the graphics area or you can enter coordinate values on the command line.

Using Cartesian (X,Y) and Polar Coordinates

In two-dimensional space, you specify points on a plane that is similar to a flat sheet of grid paper. You can enter two-dimensional coordinates as either *Cartesian (X,Y)* or *polar (distance<angle)* coordinates.

- *Cartesian coordinates* are measured from two perpendicular lines, the *X* axis and the *Y* axis. The *X* value specifies horizontal distance, and the *Y* value specifies vertical distance. The *origin* (0,0) indicates where the two lines intersect.
- *Polar coordinates* use a distance and an angle to locate a point.

You can use *absolute* or *relative* values with each method. Absolute coordinate values are based on the origin (0,0). Relative coordinate values are based on the last point entered.

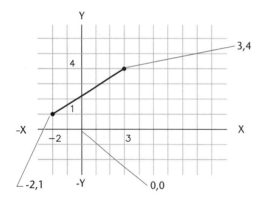

Drawing with Absolute Coordinates

Use absolute *X,Y* coordinates when you know the precise *X* and *Y* values of the location of the point. For example, the line shown at left begins at an *X* value of –2 and a *Y* value of 1 and ends at (3,4). The entries on the command line were as follows:

Command: **line**
From point: **–2,1**
To point: **3,4**

Drawing with Relative Coordinates

Use relative *X,Y* coordinates when you know the position of a point in relation to the previous point. For example, to locate a point relative to –2,1, precede the next coordinate with the @ symbol. Entering the coordinates below creates the same line as the absolute coordinates above:

Command: **line**
From point: **–2,1**
To point: **@5,3**

Drawing with Polar Coordinates

To use a polar coordinate, enter a distance and an angle, separated by an angle bracket (<). For example, to specify a point that is a distance of 1 unit from the previous point and at an angle of 45 degrees, enter **@1<45**. The line segments below were drawn with absolute and relative polar coordinates.

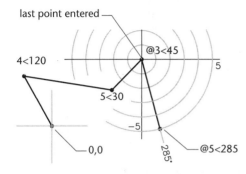

Command: **line**
From point: **0,0**
To point: **4<120**
To point: **5<30**
To point: **@3<45**
To point: **@5<285**

Because the last two points entered specify relative polar coordinates (indicated by the @ symbol), the angle and distance specified is measured from the last point entered.

AutoCAD LT displays the cursor location as coordinate values on the status bar.

`8.1134, 4.8862`

Current cursor location

ONLINE HELP UNITS, UCS, COORDS

Snapping to Precise Points on Objects

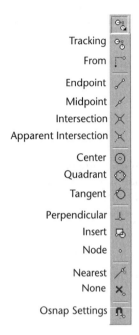

Tracking
From
Endpoint
Midpoint
Intersection
Apparent Intersection
Center
Quadrant
Tangent
Perpendicular
Insert
Node
Nearest
None
Osnap Settings

**The object
snap flyout**

**The object
snap menu**

Using *object snaps* is a quick way to specify an exact location on an object without having to know the coordinate or draw construction lines. For example, you can use an object snap to draw a line to the center of a circle, to the midpoint of a polyline segment, or to an imaginary intersection.

You can specify an object snap whenever AutoCAD LT prompts for a point. When you move your pointing device over an object, AutoCAD LT identifies active snap points with markers and labels called tooltips.

Using Single Object Snaps

When AutoCAD LT prompts for a point, you can specify single object snaps in three ways:

- *Object Snap menu*. Hold down SHIFT, right-click, and choose the object snap from the menu.
- *Standard toolbar*. Display the object snap flyout and click the button for the object snap you want.
- *Command line*. Type the object snap name or alias.

Once you have set an object snap, use the pointing device to select a location or an object.

Setting Running Object Snaps

To use the same object snap repeatedly, set it as a *running* snap. It will stay active until you turn it off. For example, you might set Center as a running snap if you need to connect the centers of a series of circles with a line.

You can set multiple running object snaps, such as Endpoint and Center. To cycle through all the snap points available for a particular object, press TAB.

Setting multiple running object snaps may have unexpected results. To turn running object snaps on and off quickly, click Osnap on the status bar, press CTRL+F, or press F3.

Changing AutoSnap Settings

AutoSnap is the feature that visually identifies object snap points. When you specify a single object snap or turn on running object snaps, AutoSnap is automatically turned on. You can change the AutoSnap settings to alter the behavior of AutoCAD LT when the cursor moves over object snap points. You can determine the size and color of the marker used to display an object snap location. You can also turn off the marker, the tooltip, or the magnetic action that locks the cursor onto the snap point.

To get started		
Action	Menu	Toolbar
Using single object snaps	SHIFT+right-click for object snap menu	Standard, object snap flyout
Setting running object snaps	Tools ➤ Drafting Settings	Standard, object snap flyout
Changing AutoSnap settings	Tools ➤ Drafting Settings	Standard, object snap flyout

ONLINE HELP OSNAP, APERTURE, DSETTINGS

Object Snap Descriptions

The table below illustrates the object snaps described in the previous topic.

Object snap descriptions		Snaps to
Object snap		**Snaps to**
Endpoint	 endpoints	Object endpoints
Midpoint	 midpoints	Object midpoints
Intersection	 intersections/extended intersections	Object intersections or locations where intersections would occur if objects were extended
Apparent Intersection	 apparent intersection	Apparent intersections of objects that do not intersect in 3D space but appear to intersect in the drawing display
Center	 centers	Center points of circles, arcs, or ellipses
Node	 nodes on line and object	Point objects created with the POINT command

Object snap		Snaps to
Quadrant	quadrants	Quadrants of arcs, circles, or ellipses
Insertion	R129 4.7K insertion point for a block	Insertion point of a block, text, attribute, or attribute definition
Perpendicular	perpendiculars	Points on objects that form a perpendicular alignment with the last point created
Tangent	tangents	Point on a circle or arc that, when connected to the last point, forms a line tangent to the object
Nearest		Object snap point closest to the selection point
None		No object snaps for the next point

Drawing Quickly with Ortho and Polar Settings

These aids can help you work quickly when drawing or editing:

- *Ortho* restricts the cursor to horizontal or vertical movement.
- *Polar tracking* displays tracking guides at specified angles.
- *Polar snap* restricts cursor movement to specified distances.

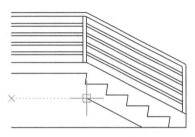

Ortho restricts cursor movement
to horizontal and vertical

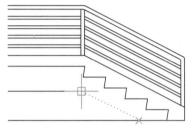

Polar tracking restricts cursor
movement to a specific angle

Using Ortho

As you draw lines or move objects, you can use *Ortho* to restrict the movement of the cursor to the horizontal or vertical axis. For example, you can
create a series of perpendicular lines by turning on Ortho before you start
drawing. Because the lines are constrained to the horizontal and vertical
axes, you can draw faster, knowing that the lines are perpendicular.

Using the Polar Tracking and Polar Snap Settings

When you are creating or modifying objects, you can use polar settings to
draw specified angles and distances. You can specify polar angle and distance
in the Drafting Settings dialog box.

- *Polar tracking restricts cursor movement to specified angular
  increments.* Once you set the tracking angle, a polar extension line is displayed at 0 degrees and at increments of the specified angle. For example,
  if the snap angle value is 15 degrees, the guideline appears at 0, 15, 30, 45,
  and so on. Polar tracking is an alternative to Ortho and is active only
  when Ortho is off.
- *Polar snap restricts cursor movement to increments of a length you
  specify.* For example, if you specify a length of 4 units, the cursor snaps
  from the first point specified to lengths of 4, 8, 12, 16, and so on. Polar
  snap is an alternative to Snap and is active only when Snap is off and polar
  tracking is on.

AutoCAD LT overrides Ortho, polar tracking, and polar snap when you enter coordinate values on the command line or specify an object snap.

Using Direct Distance Entry

Instead of entering coordinate values, you can use direct distance entry to specify a point. Using direct distance entry is a good way to specify a line length quickly—by moving the cursor to indicate a direction and then entering the distance from the first point. When Ortho is on, using direct distance entry helps you draw perpendicular lines efficiently.

When you use direct distance entry, AutoCAD LT overrides Polar Snap.

NOTE You can turn Ortho, polar tracking, and polar snap on and off quickly by clicking the Polar or Ortho buttons on the status bar.

To get started		
Action	**Menu**	**Dialog box tab**
Using polar settings	Tools ➤ Drafting Settings	Polar Tracking, Snap and Grid

ONLINE HELP ORTHO, DSETTINGS

Working with Isometric and 3D Objects

AutoCAD LT has limited three-dimensional capabilities. However, you can use *isometric drawing* to create two dimensional drawings that represent 3D objects. Isometric drawings are not true 3D drawings because they cannot be viewed in perspective or from another angle. You can also use AutoCAD LT to view and perform some basic functions with true 3D objects that were created in AutoCAD.

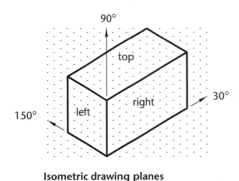

Isometric drawing planes

Isometric Drawing

Using the Isometric Snap/Grid setting helps you align each isometric plane along three major axes. If the snap angle is 0, the axes of the isometric planes are 30°, 90°, and 150°. Each plane has an associated pair of axes:

- *Left* orients the snap and grid alignment along the 90- and 150-degree axes.
- *Top* orients the snap and grid alignment along the 30- and 150-degree axes.
- *Right* orients the snap and grid alignment along the 90- and 30-degree axes.

Working on Isometric Planes

The isometric plane affects cursor movement when Snap is on and the snap style is Isometric. Choosing an isometric plane causes the snap intervals, grid, and crosshairs to realign along the corresponding isometric axes. So, when Ortho is on, the points you select when drawing objects align along the plane on which you are drawing. Therefore, you can draw the top plane of a model, switch to the left plane to draw another side, and switch to the right plane to complete the drawing. You can cycle through the isometric planes by pressing CTRL+E or F5.

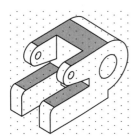

Top plane

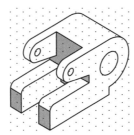

Left plane

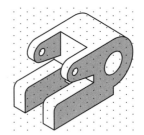

Right plane

Working with 3D Objects

AutoCAD LT supports limited modification of 3D objects created in AutoCAD. For example, you can work with a shaded 3D cube by turning off the shading and exposing the edges of the underlying *wireframe*. You can use the 3D VIEWPOINT options to view the part from various angles. Using object snaps, you can snap to points on the wireframe. You can also perform basic editing tasks such as moving the cube, changing the layer it is drawn on, and copying and pasting it to another location.

You can also approximate 3D modeling. For example, you can simulate simple 3D surfaces for visualization by specifying a thickness value for objects drawn in 2D. Or you can use wireframe modeling to create an accurate representation of a real-world object by drawing its edges in 3D.

To get started		
Action	**Menu**	**Dialog box tab**
Setting snap style to Isometric	Tools ➤ Drafting Settings	Snap and Grid

ONLINE HELP DSETTINGS, ISOPLANE, SHADEMODE

Working with User-Defined Coordinate Systems

AutoCAD LT provides two coordinate systems: a fixed coordinate system called the World Coordinate System (WCS) and a moveable coordinate system called the user coordinate system (UCS). When you begin a drawing, the UCS coincides with the WCS. However, you can reorient the UCS at will. Changing the UCS does not affect your viewpoint. It changes only the orientation and tilt of the coordinate system.

- **Moving the UCS** makes it easier to work on particular sections of your drawing and to create ordinate dimensions.
- **Rotating the UCS** helps you specify points in 3D or rotated views.

Rotated UCS icon

The UCS Icon

By default, AutoCAD LT displays an icon that indicates the current coordinate system in the lower-left corner of the graphics area. The icon represents the orientation of the UCS axes and the location of the current UCS origin. You can choose one of three styles of icon to represent the UCS. The default, 3D UCS icon, is shown on this page. Optionally, you can use the 2D UCS icon or the shaded UCS icon instead.

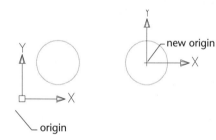

New origin moves the UCS

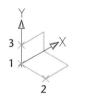

points specified for new UCS   new UCS

New origin and direction of X and Y axes rotates the UCS

Locating a New UCS Origin

By locating a new origin, you can adjust coordinate entry to be relevant to a specific area in your drawing. For example, you might relocate the origin to a corner of a building. Or, you can move the origin to the corner of a part for accurate ordinate dimensioning of holes.

Shifting the *XY* Plane

You shift the *XY* plane by specifying a UCS origin and the direction of its positive *X* and *Y* axes. This is particularly useful for working on sections where the baseline deviates from a horizontal or vertical orientation. Snap, Grid, and Ortho all rotate in line with the new UCS. For example, if you have created a 3D wireframe box, you can draw circles on each of its six sides easily by aligning the coordinate system with each side as you edit it.

Using Multiple User Coordinate Systems

You can define and save multiple user coordinate systems and restore them when needed. You can save and name UCS locations, each having a different origin and orientation, for various drawing requirements. If you do not want to define your own UCS, you can choose from several preset coordinate systems in the UCS Orientation dialog box.

You can define a UCS in a layout as well as in model space. For example, you can create a different UCS for each layout associated with a drawing file.

NOTE Only one UCS is current at any given time, and all coordinate input and display is relative to the current UCS.

To get started		
Action	**Menu**	**Toolbar**
Creating a user coordinate system Reverting to the World Coordinate System	Tools ➤ New UCS	UCS
Moving the user coordinate system Restoring a saved user coordinate system	Tools ➤ Move UCS	UCS II

ONLINE HELP UCS, UCSICON, SHADEMODE

Arrange views of your model in
viewports to make drawing easier.

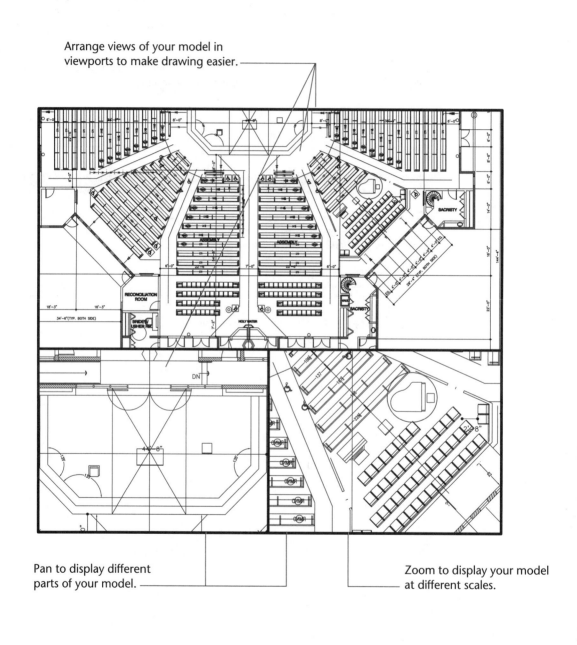

Pan to display different
parts of your model.

Zoom to display your model
at different scales.

Changing Views

7

A specific magnification, position, and orientation is known as a *view*. In this chapter, you learn to use AutoCAD LT®viewing options to display your drawings so they are easy to manipulate and plot.

When you change a view, you do not change the actual size of the drawing. You *zoom* and *pan* to change the apparent size and position. For efficiency while working, you can use *model space viewports* to show multiple views of a drawing. For plotting, you can arrange various views in paper space layouts using *layout viewports*. In addition, you can save particular views and layout configurations as named views and restore them when needed.

In this chapter

- Zooming to Magnify a View
- Panning to Reposition a View
- Using Viewports
- Saving and Restoring Views

Zooming to Magnify a View

The most common way to change a view is *zooming*. Zooming increases or decreases the apparent size of the image displayed.

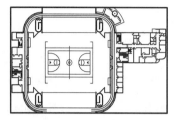

Zoomed out

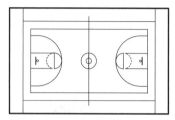

Zoomed in

Zooming in Real Time

You can use a pointing device to zoom in real time—that is, to zoom in or out by moving the cursor. Within the ZOOM command, move the cursor up to zoom in; move it down to zoom out. If you use a wheel mouse, push the top of the wheel forward to zoom in and pull it backward to zoom out.

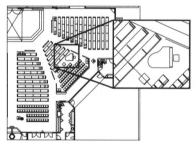

Zoom window

Defining the Zoom Window

You can quickly zoom in on a specific area by using the mouse to define a rectangular zoom window. The area you define is centered in the new display.

Using Other Zoom Options

There are a number of helpful AutoCAD LT zoom options:

- *Zooming to the center of your drawing*. ZOOM Center moves a specific point in your drawing to the center of the graphics area or a viewport.
- *Displaying the extents of the drawing objects*. ZOOM Extents displays all of the objects in the drawing, which may extend beyond grid limits.
- *Displaying the drawing boundaries*. ZOOM All displays a view based on the drawing limits.
- *Displaying a previous view*. ZOOM Previous quickly restores up to 10 prior views.
- *Using an aerial view finder to zoom*. Aerial View displays a view of the drawing in a separate window so you can quickly move to a specific area.

Scaling the View Precisely

You may need to scale a view precisely when plotting or relatively when drawing. Using ZOOM Scale, you can change the magnification in the following ways:

- **Relative to the current view.** For example, 2x displays the image at twice current size. This method is normally used in model space to change the size of the model as needed for precision drawing.
- **Relative to the drawing layout.** For example, 2xp displays the image at twice paper-space units; 1/48xp displays the image at 1:48 scale on the drawing sheet that is represented by the layout. See page 244 for more information.

NOTE If you have trouble finding your drawing on the screen, ZOOM Extents displays it all.

To get started		
Action	**Menu**	**Toolbar**
Zooming	View ➤ Zoom	Standard

ONLINE HELP ZOOM, DSVIEWER

Panning to Reposition a View

Panning is another common way to change a view. Panning moves the position of the drawing in any two-dimensional direction.

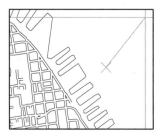

Before PAN

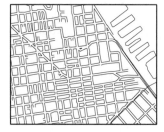

After PAN

Panning in Real Time

You can pan in real time—that is, use the pointing device to move the drawing. Within the PAN command, hold down the button and drag the drawing image to a new location. If you use a wheel mouse, hold the wheel down to pan.

Panning with an Aerial View Finder

You can display a view of the drawing in a separate Aerial View window so you can quickly move to a specific area. Drag the view box to a new location without changing its size.

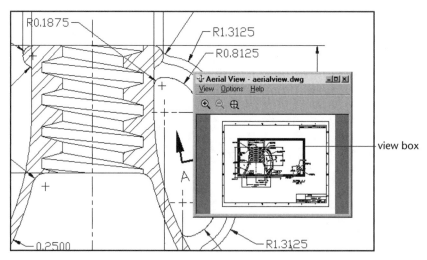

The Aerial View window in the graphics area

To zoom using Aerial View, you change the size of the view box. In addition, you can zoom in and out in the Aerial View window itself.

To get started		
Action	**Menu**	**Toolbar**
Panning	View ➤ Pan	Standard

ONLINE HELP PAN, DSVIEWER

Using Viewports

Viewports come in two varieties, with two different purposes—viewing or plotting:

- *Model space viewports* enable you to see more than one view of your drawing at one time while working in model space.
- *Layout viewports* allow you to arrange one or more views of your drawing in a layout for printing or plotting.

Using Model Space Viewports for Viewing

To begin a new drawing, you usually start with a single model space viewport that fills the entire graphics area. You can split the graphics area to display several viewports simultaneously. Model space viewports show the progress of your work from different views. They are *tiled*—that is, they completely fill the graphics area and do not overlap. As you draw, changes made in one viewport are instantly reflected in the others. You can switch among model space viewports at any time, including in the middle of a command.

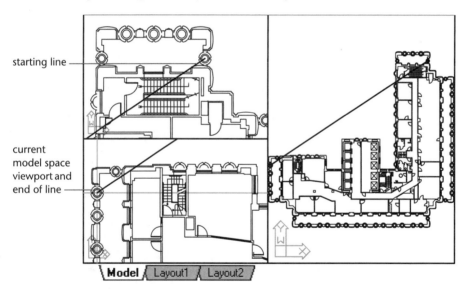

starting line

current model space viewport and end of line

View of a screen with three model space viewports

Only the currently selected model space viewport can be printed or plotted.

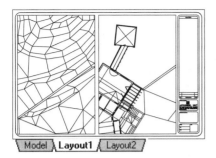

Two layout viewports, one with terrain layer frozen

Using Layout Viewports for Plotting

To lay out your drawing, you can use one or more viewports in paper space. Layout viewports do not have to be tiled; they can *float*—that is, they can overlap and do not need to fill the drawing sheet. You can resize viewport boundaries by selecting the viewport and dragging a corner.

To work on the model displayed in a viewport, double-click within the viewport. You can then zoom and pan the view in the viewport so that it is displayed on the screen exactly as you want it to be plotted. You can also freeze or turn off layers in some layout viewports without affecting others. For more information about layouts, see page 259.

To get started	
Action	**Menu**
Creating viewports	View ➤ Viewports ➤ New Viewports

ONLINE HELP MVIEW, VPORTS, ZOOM

Saving and Restoring Views

In the course of zooming and panning around your drawing, you may want to save a particular view. You can name and save a view you want to reuse—making it a *named view*. For example, you can save a view of a room in a floor plan and then restore the view whenever you want to work on it. When you save a view, the viewing position and scale are saved along with other information such as grid and snap settings. When you no longer need the view, you can delete it.

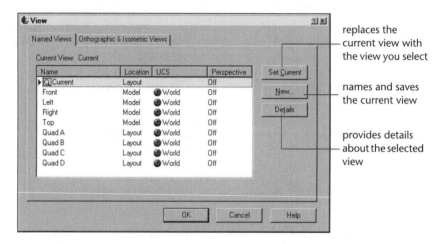

replaces the current view with the view you select

names and saves the current view

provides details about the selected view

Saving and Restoring Views in Viewports

You can save and restore the views inside individual viewports. This feature works in both model space viewports and layout viewports. What you save is the position, magnification, and orientation of the model as it is displayed in the viewport.

When you save and restore views in viewports, you work with one viewport at a time. When restored, the saved view replaces the view in the selected viewport. For example, you might save a zoomed-in view in a model space viewport, switch to paper space, create a layout viewport, and restore the saved view in the new layout viewport.

Saving and Restoring Portions of Layouts

If you want to save a view of only part of the current layout, you specify a rectangular area and save the view within the rectangular area. The view may include one or more layout viewports, portions of layout viewports, and the views that are visible in those viewports.

When you restore the named view, its zoom and pan position replaces the view displayed on your screen. For example, your layout may represent a large drawing sheet that includes multiple views of an airport. You can create four views of the layout representing four quarters of the drawing sheet. When you restore a view, you effectively zoom in on a portion of the layout, which you can then print or plot to a smaller size drawing sheet.

Saving and Restoring Viewport Configurations

You can save viewport configurations in model space. When you save viewport configurations, you save the number of viewports, their position in the graphics area, and the zoom scale that is used in each viewport.

The Layout tabs in AutoCAD LT 2000i provide a means of saving and restoring viewport configurations in paper space. For each drawing file, you can create and save multiple layouts, each with its own configuration of layout viewports.

To get started		
Action	**Menu**	**Toolbar**
Saving and restoring views	View ➤ Named Views	View
Saving and restoring viewport configurations	View ➤ Viewports	Viewports

ONLINE HELP VIEW, VPORT, MVIEW

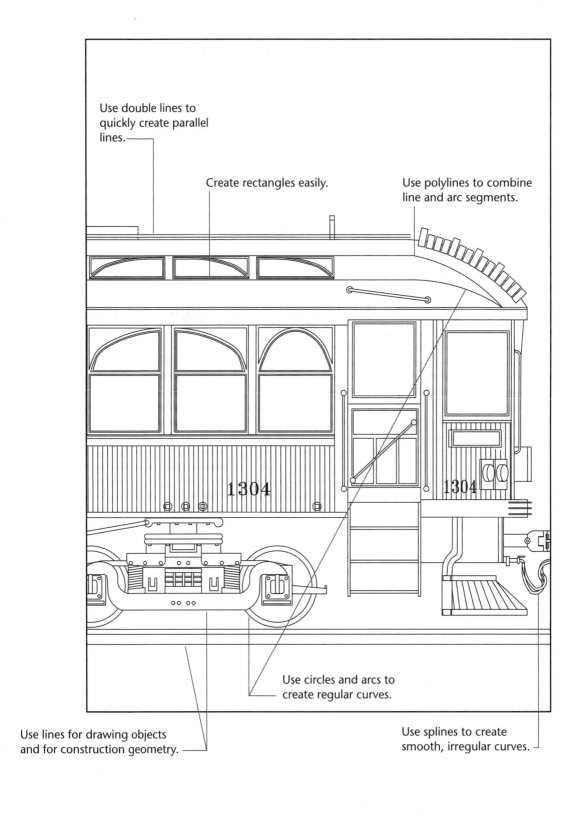

Use double lines to quickly create parallel lines.

Create rectangles easily.

Use polylines to combine line and arc segments.

1304

1304

Use circles and arcs to create regular curves.

Use lines for drawing objects and for construction geometry.

Use splines to create smooth, irregular curves.

Drawing Objects

AutoCAD LT®drawings are made up of objects—lines, circles, spline curves, ellipses, polygons, and other geometric shapes that you use to create the final composition. In general, you draw objects by specifying points with the pointing device or by entering coordinate values on the command line. Each object you create is an individual entity: that is, you can manipulate it separately from all the other objects in your drawing.

In this chapter

- Object Properties Overview
- Drawing Lines
- Drawing Polylines and Polygons
- Drawing Circles and Arcs
- Drawing Ellipses, Donuts, and Splines
- Creating Construction Geometry
- Creating Regions

Object Properties Overview

All objects created in AutoCAD LT have *properties*. Object properties are settings that control the appearance and geometric characteristics of an object. The eight general properties that are common to all objects are listed below. All other object properties are specific to the type of object.

- *Color*
- *Layer*
- *Linetype*

- *Linetype scale*
- *Plot style*
- *Thickness*

- *Hyperlink*
- *Lineweight*

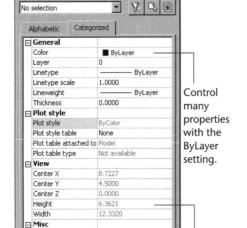

Control many properties with the ByLayer setting.

Enter new property here.

View a description of the selected property here.

Setting Object Properties

You set object properties using these methods:

- *By layer*. Properties assigned to the layer that objects are drawn on are assigned automatically to the objects themselves.
- *Individual properties*. Properties are assigned to objects individually, regardless of the layer that they are drawn on.
- *By block*. Assignment of properties can be flexible for objects in blocks. For more information, see page 190.

Selecting a property when no objects are selected sets the property for all objects you create after that. You can also modify the properties of objects that have already been created. For more information, see page 174.

Using the Properties Window

The Properties window is the main tool for setting, viewing, and modifying the properties of AutoCAD LT objects. Leaving the window open in the graphics area keeps it handy.

When you select an object in the AutoCAD LT graphics area, the Properties window displays the properties of that object. If you select multiple objects, the Properties window displays all the properties they have in common. If you select objects that were created in AutoCAD, properties you cannot change in AutoCAD LT are unavailable.

Using the Object Properties Toolbar

The Object Properties toolbar provides convenient access to object properties. By default, the toolbar is displayed above the graphics area. You use the controls to set and modify properties—and to view the properties of selected objects. The Object Properties Toolbar also includes two buttons. Use the Layer Properties Manager button to make adjustments to drawing layers.

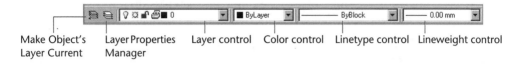

Make Object's Layer Current   Layer Properties Manager   Layer control   Color control   Linetype control   Lineweight control

---

NOTE You can use *plot styles* to override some properties. Assigning a plot style to an object or layer sets properties such as color and lineweight. Only the appearance of plotted objects is affected. For information, see page 248.

To get started		
Action	**Menu**	**Toolbar**
Setting properties	Tools ➤ Properties Modify ➤ Properties	Standard

ONLINE HELP   PROPERTIES, CHPROP, COLOR, LAYER, LINETYPE

Drawing Lines

The line is the most basic object in AutoCAD LT. In addition to *lines*, you can draw *double lines* and *polylines*. A line can be one segment or a series of connected segments, but each segment is a separate line object. Use a line if you want to edit individual segments. If you need to draw a series of line segments as a single object, use a polyline, described in the next topic. A double line is often used for drawing walls in floorplans.

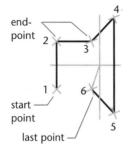

Drawing Lines

To draw a line segment, you specify a start point (1) and an endpoint (2). To continue drawing line segments, as in the example at left, you continue to specify points in your drawing (3, 4, 5, and 6). Press ENTER to end the line at 6, or enter **c** (Close) to connect the start point of the first segment (1) with the endpoint of the last (6).

For step-by-step instructions on drawing lines, see page 56.

Drawing Double Lines

Start point

Endpoint

To draw a double-line segment, you specify a start point (1) and an endpoint (2). You can continue to add new segments (3) until you exit the command. To connect the last segment to the starting point, enter **c** (Close). The example shows a new segment, with the last segment closing the double line.

You can draw double lines as straight segments or as arcs. Each double-line segment and endcap, a line that connects the double-line endpoints, is actually a separate line object that you can edit individually.

New segment

Line closed

You can control the placement and appearance of double lines using command line options. For example, you can specify the width to determine the amount of offset between lines. You can also connect or cap specified ends of double lines.

Double lines are centered on or offset from an imaginary line called a *dragline*. You specify the relationship between the double line and the dragline.

Using Other AutoCAD LT Tools to Create Parallel Lines

An offset line is an exact replica of a line that is drawn at a specified distance from the original line. Double lines create offset lines simultaneously. You can also use the OFFSET command to create parallel lines as well as concentric circles and parallel curves. For information about offsetting, see page 162.

The Ortho setting helps you to easily create parallel and perpendicular lines. For information about using Ortho for quick precision drawing, see page 118.

To get started		
Action	**Menu**	**Toolbar**
Drawing lines	Draw ➤ Line	Draw
Drawing double Lines	Draw ➤ Double Line	Draw

ONLINE HELP LINE, DLINE, OFFSET

Drawing Polylines and Polygons

A *polyline* is a connected sequence of line or arc segments created as a single object. Use polylines if you want to edit all segments at once. For flexibility, you can also edit polyline segments singly.

Polygons are closed polylines with between 3 and 1,024 equal-length sides. Because polygons always have equal-length sides, they provide a simple way to draw squares and equilateral triangles.

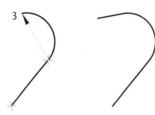

Endpoint of arc   Final segment

Drawing Polylines

To draw a polyline segment, you specify a start point and an endpoint. To draw additional segments, continue to specify points in your drawing. Also, you can include arcs in polylines. As the example shows, you draw a polyline segment (1 and 2), then switch to Arc mode by entering **a**, and continue with an arc segment (3). Enter **L** to return to Line mode, and then draw a tangential line segment.

You can draw polylines of various widths by using the Width and Halfwidth options after you specify a starting point for a polyline. You can also make polyline segments taper, and you can close the polyline.

Uniform width   Mixed width   Tapered segment

Drawing Polygons

You can draw a polygon by specifying the number of sides, and then

- Specifying the center of the polygon (1), entering **i** (Inscribed), and specifying radius length (2). AutoCAD LT creates a polygon whose endpoints are inscribed inside the specified radius.
- Specifying the center of the polygon (3), entering **c** (Circumscribed), and specifying radius length (4). AutoCAD LT creates a polygon whose endpoints are circumscribed around the specified radius.
- Specifying the endpoints (5 and 6) of one of the edges of the polygon. AutoCAD LT creates a polygon with equal sides of the specified length.

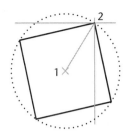  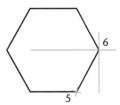

Inscribed option   **Circumscribed option**   **Endpoint option**

NOTE You can create a closed polyline from the boundaries of overlapping objects that form a closed area. See page 148 for information.

To get started		
Action	**Menu**	**Toolbar**
Drawing polylines	Draw ➤ Polyline	Draw
Drawing polygons	Draw ➤ Polygon	Draw

ONLINE HELP PLINE, POLYGON, RECTANG

Drawing Circles and Arcs

You can create a variety of basic curved objects with AutoCAD LT, including circles and arcs.

Drawing Circles

To create circles, use one of the following methods:

- Specify the center and radius (default method).
- Specify the center and diameter.
- Define the circumference of the circle with two or three points.
- Create the circle tangent to two existing objects.
- Create the circle tangent to two objects and specify a radius.

In the following illustrations, the darker circles are the examples.

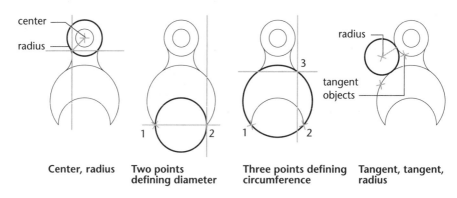

Center, radius   Two points defining diameter   Three points defining circumference   Tangent, tangent, radius

Drawing Arcs

To create arcs, you can specify various combinations of center, endpoint, start point, radius, angle, chord length, and direction values. The examples illustrate three ways to specify two points and an included angle.

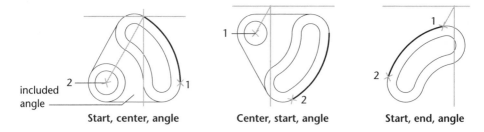

Start, center, angle   Center, start, angle   Start, end, angle

endpoint
of line

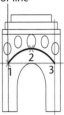

Arc drawn
using default
3-point
method

The example at left illustrates how you draw an arc by the default method—specifying three points. Using *object snaps*, you can connect objects you are drawing to precise points on other objects. For the arc, you can snap to the endpoint of a line for the first point (1), to the quadrant of a circle for the second point (2), and to the endpoint of a line for the arc endpoint (3). For information about snapping to precise points on objects, see page 114.

You can use the LINE command immediately after completing an arc to start the line at the arc endpoint. You can also connect sequentially drawn arcs or start an arc at a line endpoint immediately after completing the line.

NOTE The FILLET command creates an arc tangent to two existing objects. For more information, see page 170. Also, you can draw free-form sequential arcs easily by using the REVCLOUD command. See page 178.

To get started		
Action	**Menu**	**Toolbar**
Drawing circles	Draw ➤ Circle	Draw
Drawing arcs	Draw ➤ Arc	Draw

ONLINE HELP CIRCLE, ARC, ANGDIR

Drawing Ellipses, Donuts, and Splines

Ellipses and elliptical arcs are useful for creating conic sections. They can also be used to represent circles and arcs that are viewed at an angle in isometric drawings. Drawing *donuts* is a quick way to create filled rings or solid-filled circles. *Splines* are useful for creating irregularly shaped curves.

Drawing Ellipses

The illustrations below show two ellipses drawn by specifying the longer axis (1 and 2), called the *major* axis, and a distance (3) and by specifying the shorter axis (1 and 2), called the *minor* axis, and a distance (3).

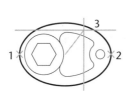

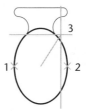

First axis of ellipse as major axis   **First axis of ellipse as minor axis**

Drawing Elliptical Arcs

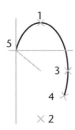

The default method of drawing elliptical arcs uses the first axis endpoints and the second axis distance, as for full ellipses. You then specify start and end angles. These angles define the start and end points of the elliptical arc. In the example, start and end angles are measured from point 1, which is the start point of the first axis. The ANGDIR system variable determines that the angles are measured counterclockwise from point 1. Point 2 is the second endpoint of the first axis, and point 3 is the distance of the second axis. The start angle (4) is 230 degrees and the end angle (5) is 50 degrees.

Drawing Donuts

To create a donut, specify the inside and outside diameters (1 and 2) and the location of the center point (3). You can continue creating multiple copies with the same diameter by specifying different center points.

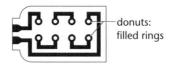

donuts:
filled rings

donut:
solid-filled
circle

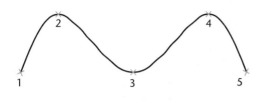

Drawing Spline Curves

You specify points to create a spline. AutoCAD LT draws a smooth curve that passes through or near the points. You can change the spline-fitting *tolerance*, which determines how closely the curve fits the points. The lower the tolerance, the closer the fit. The example illustrates zero tolerance.

NOTE You can create a spline from a polyline. For information, see page 172.

To get started		
Action	**Menu**	**Toolbar**
Drawing ellipses	Draw ➤ Ellipse	Draw
Drawing donuts	Draw ➤ Donut	
Drawing splines	Draw ➤ Spline	Draw

ONLINE HELP ELLIPSE, DONUT, SPLINE, ANGDIR

Creating Construction Geometry

You can create construction lines called *xlines* that extend to infinity in both directions, or *rays* that extend infinitely in one direction. Xlines and rays are used as handy references for creating other objects. For example, you can use them as guidelines when drawing multiple views of a model, or to find the center of a triangle. You can also use them to create object snap points that assist you in drawing precisely.

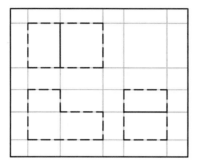

Orthographic projection using Xlines

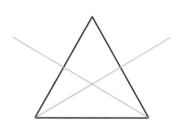

The center of a triangle found using rays

You can use other geometry, such as lines and circles, as construction geometry. For example, *point objects* can act as reference locations when you divide objects into equally spaced or proportionally spaced segments. You can also snap to point objects using the Node object snap.

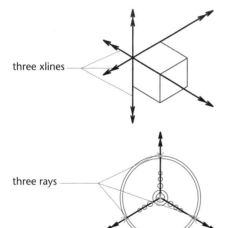

three xlines

three rays

Creating Xlines

To create an xline, you can specify its orientation in one of several ways. The default is the two-point method: you select two points to define the orientation. The first point, the root, is considered the midpoint of the construction line.

Creating Rays

To create a ray, specify the starting point and a point through which the ray must pass. Because rays extend in only one direction, using them helps reduce the visual clutter caused by numerous xlines.

Creating Points

You create a point object by specifying its location with the pointing device or by entering a coordinate value on the command line. To set the style and size of the point, use the Point Style dialog box. You can set the size relative to the screen or in absolute units.

NOTE Xlines and rays are ignored by commands that display drawing extents.

To get started		
Action	**Menu**	**Toolbar**
Creating xlines	Draw ➤ Construction Line	Draw
Creating rays	Draw ➤ Ray	Draw
Creating point objects	Draw ➤ Point	Draw
Setting point style	Format ➤ Point Style	Draw

ONLINE HELP   XLINE, RAY, POINT, DDPTYPE

Creating Regions

Regions are two-dimensional objects you create from objects that singly or in combination enclose an area. These objects can be lines, polylines, arcs, circles, elliptical arcs, ellipses, and splines. Existing regions can be combined to form complex closed objects.

Regions possess physical properties such as centroids or centers of mass, moments, and products of inertia. You can display these values. Regions help you calculate the area of combined objects.

Creating Regions

To create a region, use the REGION or the BOUNDARY command.

- REGION converts the closed objects you select to a new region object. The original objects are replaced by the region object.
- BOUNDARY creates a new region from the boundaries of objects. This method leaves the original objects in the drawing.

Combining Regions

To combine regions using Boolean operations, use one of these commands:

- SUBTRACT produces a new region composed of one or more areas subtracted from another region.

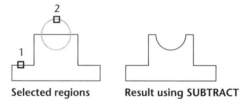

Selected regions   Result using SUBTRACT

- UNION produces a new region composed of the combined areas of two or more regions.

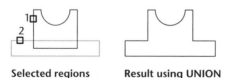

Selected regions   Result using UNION

- INTERSECT produces a new region composed of the overlapping areas common to two or more regions.

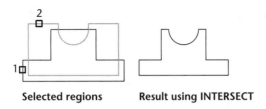

Selected regions   **Result using INTERSECT**

NOTE The BOUNDARY command can be useful for creating closed polylines from the edges of objects that bound an area.

To get started		
Action	**Menu**	**Toolbar**
Creating regions	Draw ➤ Region	Draw

ONLINE HELP REGION, BOUNDARY, MASSPROP, AREA, UNION, SUBTRACT, INTERSECT

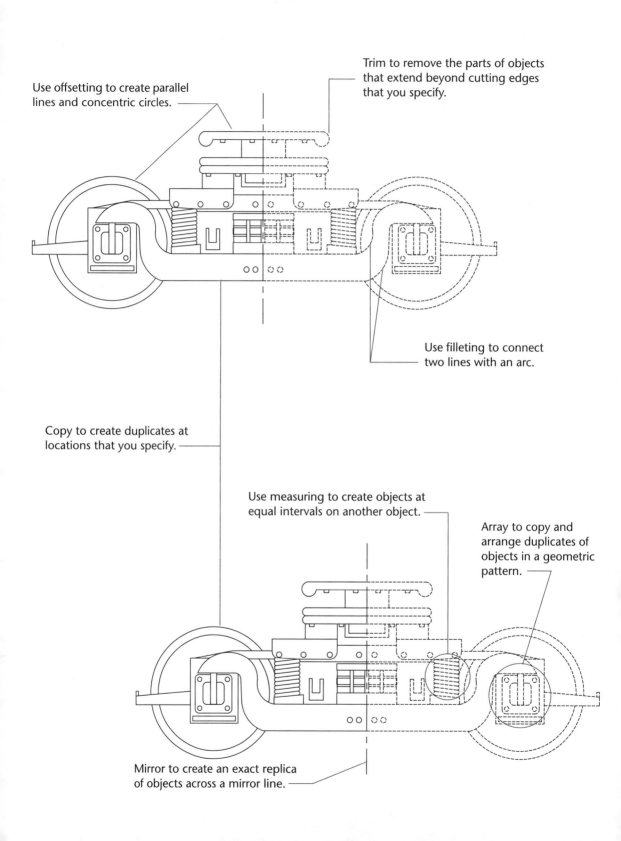

Use offsetting to create parallel lines and concentric circles.

Trim to remove the parts of objects that extend beyond cutting edges that you specify.

Use filleting to connect two lines with an arc.

Copy to create duplicates at locations that you specify.

Use measuring to create objects at equal intervals on another object.

Array to copy and arrange duplicates of objects in a geometric pattern.

Mirror to create an exact replica of objects across a mirror line.

Making Modifications

9

AutoCAD LT® provides powerful tools for modifying objects: you can change an object's size, shape, and location, or you can connect objects by creating corners with lines or arcs. You can also display, modify, and apply properties to selected objects. For more information on setting object properties, see page 136. This chapter describes how to edit two-dimensional (2D) objects.

This chapter also includes information on editing aids such as markups, groups, and revision clouds. Additional topics cover analyzing drawing geometry and removing data that is no longer needed from the *definition tables* stored in drawing files.

In this chapter

- Reviewing Electronic Markups
- Selecting Objects to Edit
- Erasing, Breaking, and Trimming Objects
- Measuring and Dividing Objects
- Extending Objects
- Duplicating Objects
- Arraying Objects
- Moving and Rotating Objects
- Stretching and Scaling Objects
- Chamfering and Filleting Corners
- Editing Polylines and Splines
- Modifying Properties
- Working with Saved Layer Settings
- Using Editing Aids
- Analyzing Drawings
- Purging Unneeded Information

Reviewing Electronic Markups

Before making modifications to drawings, you might want to review the electronic markups created by members of your design team. Instead of using red ink on paper, team members can make comments and corrections with the mouse and keyboard directly on the screen using the Autodesk viewing and markup tool, Volo™ View. You can insert these *markups* into drawing files.

Working with Markup Files

Volo View users can save their markups as redline markup language (RML) files. They can create and save more than one set of markups in an RML file. For example, they can mark up the plan view of a drawing in model space and then create markups on every layout associated with that drawing. Each set of markups, for the model space plan view and for each layout, is inserted separately. For example, to insert markups that were created for a particular layout, you must have the appropriate layout tab selected. To insert the markups for model space plan view, you must have the Model tab selected.

Working with the Markup Layer

When you insert an RML file, its markup objects are added to your drawing file on a new layer, called "_Markup_". This arrangement makes it easy for you to keep markups separate from the other objects in your drawing. You can use the Layer Properties Manager to hide markups or to assign identifying properties to them. For example, you could assign a color or a linetype to the Markup layer that is not used elsewhere in the drawing.

When you insert more than one set of markups or more than one markup file into a drawing, all of the markups are placed on the Markup layer. In other words, if you have one markup file inserted, the Markup layer includes markups from that file. When you insert a second markup file, its markups are mixed with the first markups on the Markup layer. To avoid confusion, you can rename the Markup layer before inserting additional markup files. For example, you could use the layer names Markup1, Markup2, Markup3, and so on to distinguish one set of markups from another.

NOTE If you move markup objects off the Markup layer, be careful not to lose track of them. Unless you provide a mechanism for identifying them, they will be indistinguishable from the other objects in the drawing.

Working with Markup Objects

Inserting an RML file translates its markup objects to the most appropriate AutoCAD LT objects. For example, a Volo View box becomes a polyline, and a note becomes a multiline text object. Hyperlinks included in RML files are objects that are associated with other objects, such as circles. Inserting them into AutoCAD LT files results in objects, such as circles, with associated hyperlink properties. You can edit these translated objects in the same way you would any other object in the drawing file. All objects are placed using the World Coordinate System.

Inserted objects take on the properties of the Markup layer. By default, their color is red and they use the CONTINUOUS linetype. All styles applied to the markups in Volo View are ignored in AutoCAD LT, except for text height. Inserted dimension and text objects use the current AutoCAD LT style.

NOTE You can create revision clouds in AutoCAD LT to highlight markups. For more information, see page 178.

To get started	
Action	**Menu**
Inserting markup files	Insert ➤ Markup

ONLINE HELP RMLIN

Selecting Objects to Edit

Before you edit objects, you must create a *selection set* of the objects. A selection set can consist of a single object or a more complex grouping. You can create a selection set either before or after you choose the editing command.

- *Choosing the command first.* When you choose an editing command, AutoCAD LT prompts you to select objects and replaces the crosshairs with a pickbox.
- *Selecting objects first.* You can change the selection mode so you must select objects before using an editing command. You can also select objects so that they are marked with grips, which you can use for editing. For information about AutoCAD LT operating options, see page 106.

Object Selection Methods

Use these methods to select objects:

- *Select individual objects* by clicking them with a pointing device.
- *Specify a selection area or selection fence* with a pointing device.
- *Enter an option* at the Select Objects prompt on the command line.

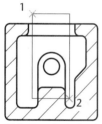

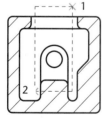

Objects selected using window selection

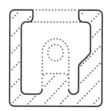

Objects selected using crossing selection

Using Selection Areas

You can select objects by enclosing them in a *rectangular* selection area. You define a rectangular selection area in the graphics area by specifying opposite corners. The order in which you specify the points makes a difference.

- *Dragging from left to right* creates a *window* selection, which selects only objects entirely within the selection area.
- *Dragging from right to left* creates a *crossing* selection, which selects objects within and crossing the selection area.

To select objects within an irregularly shaped area, you can use a *polygon* selection area. The direction in which you specify points does not matter: you specify whether to use a *window polygon* or a *crossing polygon*.

Using Selection Fences

You can select nonadjacent objects in a complex drawing most easily with a selection *fence*. A fence is a line or polyline that selects all the objects it passes through. The illustration below shows a fence selecting several components.

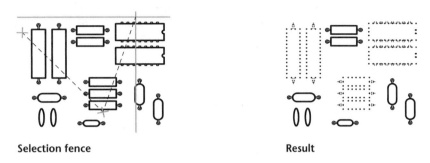

Selection fence   Result

NOTE You can organize sets of objects into named groups to streamline object selection. For information about using groups, see page 176.

To get started		
Action	**Menu**	**Dialog box tab**
Customizing object selection	Tools ➤ Options	Selection

ONLINE HELP SELECT, OPTIONS

Erasing, Breaking, and Trimming Objects

These methods delete unwanted objects, or parts of objects, from drawings:

- *Erasing* deletes the entire object.
- *Breaking* removes part of the object by breaking it at points you specify.
- *Trimming* cuts the object at a precise edge and removes the excess.

Erasing Objects

You can use all the object selection methods with the ERASE command. The example shows how you use window selection to erase a section of piping.

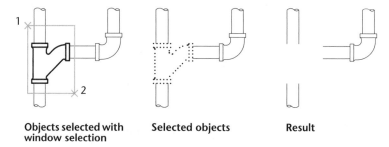

Objects selected with window selection   **Selected objects**   **Result**

Breaking Objects

When breaking an object, you can select the object at the first break point and then specify a second break point, as shown in the example. Or you can select the entire object and then specify the two break points.

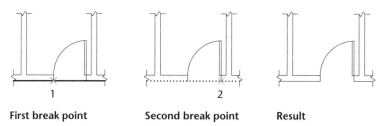

First break point   **Second break point**   **Result**

Trimming Objects

To trim, you cut an object at an edge defined by one or more objects. Objects defined as cutting edges must intersect the object to be trimmed or must intersect it if extended. In addition, an object can be *both* a cutting edge *and* an object being trimmed. If you do not specify a cutting edge, all objects could be used as cutting edges. The illustrations that follow show both actual intersections and intersections where lines would intersect if extended.

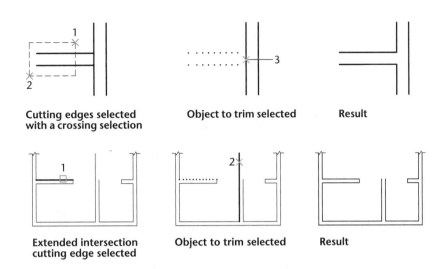

Cutting edges selected   **Object to trim selected**   **Result**
with a crossing selection

Extended intersection   **Object to trim selected**   **Result**
cutting edge selected

To get started		
Action	**Menu**	**Toolbar**
Erasing objects	Modify ➤ Erase	Modify
Breaking objects	Modify ➤ Break	Modify
Trimming objects	Modify ➤ Trim	Modify

ONLINE HELP ERASE, BREAK, TRIM

Measuring and Dividing Objects

When you need to identify specific intervals on an object, you can use the MEASURE and DIVIDE commands.

- MEASURE specifies the length of each segment.
- DIVIDE specifies the number of equal segments.

With both methods, you can identify the intervals by inserting either a point object or a named set of objects known as a *symbol* or a *block*.

- *Inserting point objects* makes it possible to use the Node object snap to align other objects at even intervals on the measured or divided object.
- *Inserting blocks* helps you create precise geometric constructions or insert custom markers.

These commands do not actually break the object into individual objects; they only identify locations on the objects.

You can measure or divide lines, arcs, splines, circles, ellipses, and polylines. The starting point for measurements or divisions varies with the object type. For example, line or polyline segments start at the endpoint closest to the selection point.

Measuring Intervals on Objects

You use the MEASURE command to mark intervals on an object. In the following illustration, an object has point objects inserted at measured intervals.

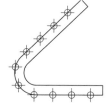

Object selected   Points at measured intervals

Dividing Objects into Equal Segments

You use the DIVIDE command to create point objects or blocks on an object at a specific number of equal intervals.

In the following illustration, an object is divided into equal segments.

Object selected　　　　　　　　**Blocks indicating divisions**

For more information about snapping to precise points on objects, see page 114. For more information about using symbols and blocks, see page 186.

To get started	
Action	**Menu**
Measuring intervals on objects	Draw ➤ Point ➤ Measure
Dividing objects into equal segments	Draw ➤ Point ➤ Divide

ONLINE HELP MEASURE, DIVIDE, DDPTYPE

Extending Objects

You can extend objects so that they end precisely at a boundary defined by other objects. You can also extend objects to where they *would* intersect a boundary. If you do not specify a boundary, all objects become potential boundaries. This is called *implied selection*. The illustration shows lines extended precisely to a circle, which is the boundary.

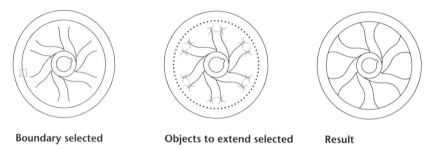

Boundary selected   Objects to extend selected   Result

Extending to an Implied Boundary

The illustration shows three horizontal lines extended to an implied boundary, where they would intersect the single line if it were extended.

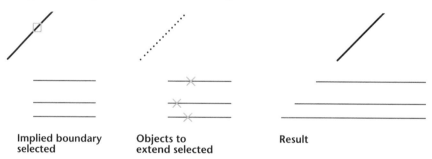

Implied boundary   Objects to   Result
selected   extend selected

Extending Polylines

You can extend polylines only if they are open. Either the first or the last segment extends as if it was a line or arc object.

Wide polylines extend so the centerline intersects the boundary. If you extend a tapered polyline segment, the width of the extended end is corrected to continue the original taper to the new endpoint, as shown in the following example.

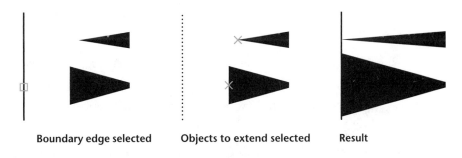

Boundary edge selected   **Objects to extend selected**   **Result**

NOTE You can change both the size and shape of objects at once using the LENGTHEN command. The results are similar to both extending and trimming, but the LENGTHEN command provides additional options.

To get started		
Action	**Menu**	**Toolbar**
Extending objects	Modify ➤ Extend	Modify
Lengthening objects	Modify ➤ Lengthen	Modify

ONLINE HELP EXTEND, LENGTHEN

Duplicating Objects

With AutoCAD LT, there are several ways to make copies of objects:

- *Copying* creates new objects at a specified location.
- *Offsetting* creates new objects at a specified distance from selected objects or through a specified point.
- *Mirroring* creates a mirror image of objects around a specified mirror line.
- *Arraying* creates sets of copies in a rectangular or circular pattern.

This topic covers copying, offsetting, and mirroring. For information about creating arrays, see page 164.

Copying Objects

You can copy objects within one drawing and also between drawings.

- *Copying objects within a drawing*. To copy within a drawing, you specify a start point for the selection set, called a *base point*. Then you specify a second point to determine the distance and direction of the copy. These points can be anywhere within the drawing. Enter **multiple** on the command line to make more than one copy.
- *Copying objects between drawings*. To copy objects from another AutoCAD LT drawing, open both drawings in AutoCAD LT and copy a selection set from one drawing to the Clipboard. Then paste the selection set from the Clipboard into the other drawing. You can also copy by dragging objects from drawing to drawing. For more information about this kind of copying, see page 222.

For more information about copying and pasting between AutoCAD LT and documents within another application, see page 234.

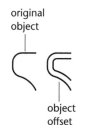

original object

object offset

Offsetting Objects

Offsetting creates a new object that seems to trace a selected object at a specified distance. Offsetting circles creates larger or smaller circles depending on the offset side. For an easy way to create parallel lines or concentric circles, use offsetting.

Mirroring Objects

You mirror objects around a mirror line, which you define with two points. You then choose to delete or retain the original objects.

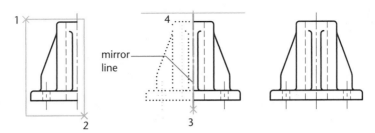

| Object selected | Mirror line defined | Result with original retained |

Mirroring is useful for creating symmetrical objects. You can quickly draw half the object and mirror it rather than draw the whole object.

To get started		
Action	**Menu**	**Toolbar**
Copying objects in a drawing	Modify ➤ Copy	Modify
Copying objects between drawings	Edit ➤ Copy	Standard
Offsetting objects	Modify ➤ Offset	Modify
Mirroring objects	Modify ➤ Mirror	Modify

ONLINE HELP COPY, COPYCLIP, PASTECLIP, OFFSET, MIRROR, MULTIPLE

Arraying Objects

You can quickly duplicate objects and arrange them in a pattern called an *array*. You control the number and orientation of these copies.

- *Polar array* arranges objects in a circular pattern.
- *Rectangular array* arranges objects in a matrix of columns and rows.

Creating Polar Arrays

The polar array view of the Array dialog box provides the options for defining a polar array, as shown below.

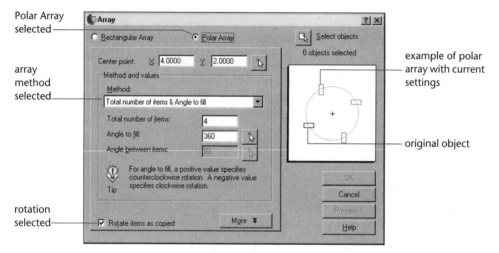

The illustration shows the selected object (1) and the results of a 360-degree polar array consisting of eight objects rotated around the center point (2).

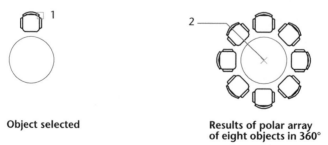

Object selected

Results of polar array of eight objects in 360°

Creating Rectangular Arrays

For rectangular arrays, you specify the number of rows and columns and the distance between the rows and columns. You can control the direction of the array by specifying positive or negative values for distances. The illustration shows the object selected and the resulting two-row, four-column array. By default, AutoCAD LT creates rectangular arrays of horizontal and perpendicular rows and columns. You can rotate an array by changing its angle.

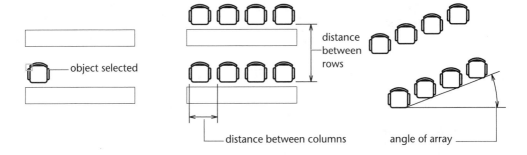

object selected

distance between rows

distance between columns

angle of array

To get started		
Action	Menu	Toolbar
Creating arrays	Modify ➤ Array	Modify

ONLINE HELP ARRAY

Moving and Rotating Objects

You can rotate objects or move them without changing orientation.

Moving Objects

To move an object, you select the object to move, specify the base point (1), and then specify a second point to determine the distance and direction of the move (2). In the illustration, these steps move the window higher and away from the door.

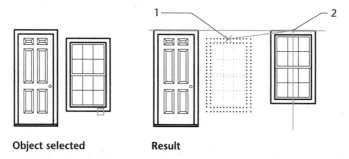

Object selected   Result

For information about moving objects by stretching them, see page 168.

Rotating Objects

You rotate objects by specifying a base point and a relative or absolute angle. You specify the rotation angle by clicking the pointing device or entering a value. You can control whether objects are rotated counterclockwise or clockwise.

- **Rotate by relative angle (default).** With the Specify Rotation Angle option, you specify an angle that is relative to the current orientation of the object you want to rotate. The rotation value is applied to the current orientation of the object being rotated. For example, if the object is currently rotated at 30 degrees, and you specify a 30-degree angle of rotation, the new rotation value for the object is 60 degrees.
- **Rotate to an absolute angle.** With the Reference option, you can specify two reference points on the object you want to rotate, and then specify an absolute angle that you want the reference points to be rotated to. The angle that you specify is the angle that the entire object is rotated to, regardless of its current orientation.

The default relative angle method is used in the following illustration. It shows how specifying the base point (1) and the angle of rotation (2) rotates a plan view of a house.

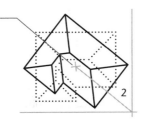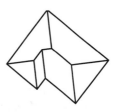

Object selected	Base point and angle of rotation	Result

To get started		
Action	**Menu**	**Toolbar**
Moving objects	Modify ➤ Move	Modify
Rotating objects	Modify ➤ Rotate	Modify

ONLINE HELP MOVE, ROTATE

Stretching and Scaling Objects

You can resize objects by stretching and scaling them.

- *Stretching an object* moves part of the object to a new location.
- *Scaling an object* changes the object's size, not its proportions.

Stretching Objects

To stretch an object, you specify what to stretch and how far to stretch it. It's very important to select the part of the object you want to stretch precisely. In the following example, you select the object with a crossing selection (1 and 2). Then specify the base point (3) and the point of displacement (4). Turning on Ortho helps move objects in a perpendicular line.

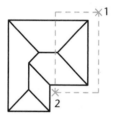 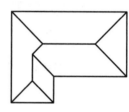 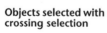

Objects selected with crossing selection   Points specified for stretch with Ortho on   Result

The following example shows how you move a door from one part of a wall to another by stretching. Again, you specify a crossing selection (1 and 2), the base point (3), and the point of displacement (4). Because the door lies entirely within the selection area, it moves. The wall lines stretch in accordance with the movement of the door.

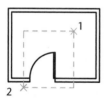 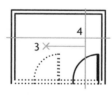 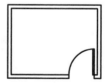

Objects selected with crossing selection   Objects dragged with Ortho on   Result

Scaling Objects

Scaling always uses the same scale factor in both the *X* and *Y* directions.

- *Scaling by a scale factor* enlarges or shrinks objects in the selection set. A scale factor larger than 1 enlarges the objects; less than 1 shrinks them.
- *Scaling by reference* uses an existing object to determine the new size. You can use this option to scale an entire model.

In the following example, you decrease the size of the block by half, scaling it by a factor of 0.5, which you enter on the command line.

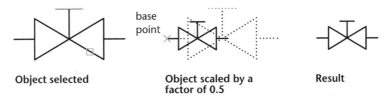

Object selected   Object scaled by a   Result
factor of 0.5

To scale by reference, specify the current length and then the length. For example, if one side of an object is 4.8 units long and you want to expand it to 7.5 units, use 4.8 as the reference length and 7.5 as the new length. Or specify a base point and two reference points and drag to specify a new scale.

To get started		
Action	**Menu**	**Toolbar**
Stretching objects	Modify ➤ Stretch	Modify
Scaling objects	Modify ➤ Scale	Modify

ONLINE HELP STRETCH, SCALE

Chamfering and Filleting Corners

Chamfering and filleting create special kinds of corners. You can chamfer and fillet lines, polylines, xlines, rays, and entire polygons. You can also chamfer or fillet every vertex of a polyline at the same time.

- *Chamfering* connects two nonparallel objects by extending or trimming them to intersect or to join with a beveled line.
- *Filleting* connects two objects with a smoothly fitted arc of a specified radius. Although an inside corner is called a *fillet,* and an outside corner is called a *round,* AutoCAD LT treats both as fillets.

Chamfering Objects

The simplest way to chamfer is to select the objects that you want to have chamfered corners. You can also chamfer by first specifying a chamfer distance or angle, which remain set until changed. Use the *distance method* to specify the distance between the new endpoint of one chamfered line and its implied intersection with the other. If the distance is zero, chamfering extends chamfered objects to meet, as shown in the following example.

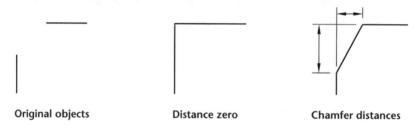

Original objects   Distance zero   Chamfer distances

With the *angle method,* you specify the first chamfer distance and then specify the angle the chamfer line forms with this object. The example shows the result of specifying a distance and an angle.

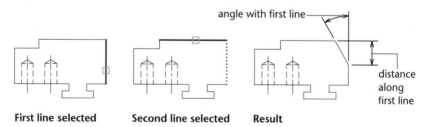

First line selected   Second line selected   Result

Filleting Objects

To fillet objects, you select them. You can also specify a fillet radius, which is the radius of the arc that connects filleted objects before selection. Changing the radius affects subsequent fillets.

To fillet line and polyline combinations, the line must intersect, or its extension must intersect, one of the polyline's line segments.

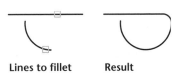

Lines to fillet   **Result**

You can also fillet splines, circles, arcs, and true ellipses. Depending on the points you specify, more than one possible fillet can exist between circles and arcs. AutoCAD LT chooses the endpoint closest to your selection point.

NOTE By default, objects are trimmed when chamfered or filleted. You can specify that the objects remain untrimmed.

To get started		
Action	**Menu**	**Toolbar**
Chamfering objects	Modify ➤ Chamfer	Modify
Filleting objects	Modify ➤ Fillet	Modify

ONLINE HELP CHAMFER, FILLET

Editing Polylines and Splines

You edit polylines and splines by relocating the points that define them.

- *Polylines* are defined by the points that begin and end each segment.
- *Spline curves* are defined by the *fit points* used to create them.

Editing Polylines

You can close or open polylines and edit them by moving, adding, or deleting individual vertices. You can also straighten the polyline between any two vertices, set a uniform width for the entire polyline, or control the width of each segment.

You can join a line, an arc, or another polyline to an open polyline if their ends connect or are within a distance you can set, called the fuzz distance. The ends are joined by either trimming them, extending them, or connecting them with a new segment.

You can create a spline curve by editing a polyline with the Spline option. The example below illustrates the results of the Spline option. Using the Decurve option changes the splined polyline back to a polyline.

Polyline

Spline-fit polyline

In the illustration below, each polyline segment has a different starting and ending width, resulting in a taper.

Polyline selected

Segments with different
start and end widths

Editing Splines

You can modify a spline by adjusting its fit points: delete them, add more for greater accuracy, or move them to alter the shape of the spline. You can open or close a spline, edit its start and end tangents, or reverse its direction. You also can change the *tolerance* of the spline, which affects how closely the spline adheres to the fit points.

You can further refine splines by adding fit points to the frame of a curve. The more control points you specify in a particular part of the frame, the more pull they exert on the curve.

As in the following example, you can use grips to edit a spline by moving a fit point. You can also use grips to reposition a point (vertex) on a polyline.

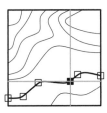 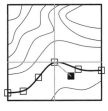 

Fit point   **Fit point moved**   **Result**

To get started		
Action	**Menu**	**Toolbar**
Editing polylines	Modify ➤ Object ➤ Polyline	Modify II
Editing splines	Modify ➤ Object ➤ Spline	Modify II

ONLINE HELP PEDIT, SPLINEDIT

Modifying Properties

You can use individual commands to change object properties such as color, layer, linetype, and lineweight. However, AutoCAD LT provides two efficient ways to manipulate object properties without using multiple commands.

- **Editing object properties.** Use the Properties window or the Object Properties toolbar to make changes efficiently.
- **Matching properties of other objects.** Use the MATCHPROP command to copy properties from one object to other objects.

For more information about object properties, the Properties window, and the Object Properties toolbar, see page 136.

Editing Properties

To quickly and easily edit object properties, use one of these tools:

- **Properties window** provides a complete list of properties, so you can view an object's properties and change the ones that can be changed.
- **Object Properties toolbar** provides options for viewing or changing the properties that are common to all objects, including layer, color, linetype, lineweight, and plot style.

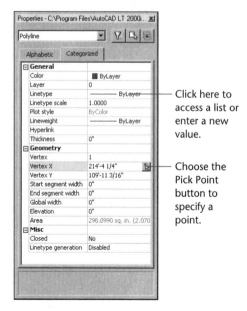

Click here to access a list or enter a new value.

Choose the Pick Point button to specify a point.

When you double-click almost any object, AutoCAD LT displays the Properties window. The Properties window consolidates object property information in one place. When you leave the Properties window open while you work, it lists the properties and the current settings for all selected objects. If you select more than one object, only the common properties are listed. To change the value for a property, click in the cell next to the name of the property. Then enter a new value or choose a value from the drop-down list, if one is available. You can cycle through values by double-clicking the property cell. In some cases, you can open a dialog box in which you can change the value. The Pick Point button changes coordinate values.

Settings you change in the Properties window take effect immediately in the drawing. You see immediate feedback in the graphics area.

The Object Properties toolbar is docked by default at the top of the graphics area. To use it to change object properties, select the object or objects you want to change and then specify new values in the controls on the toolbar.

Matching Properties

You can copy the properties of one object to other objects. First you select the object whose properties you want to copy. Then you select the objects to which you want to apply the properties. You can also use the Settings option to select the properties you want to match and clear the ones you don't. You can choose to match color, layer, linetype, linetype scale, lineweight, thickness, plot style, and in some cases dimension, text, and hatch.

For information about copying object properties between open drawings, see page 222.

To get started		
Action	**Menu**	**Toolbar**
Editing properties	Tools ➤ Properties Modify ➤ Properties	Object Properties
Matching properties	Modify ➤ Match Properties	Standard

ONLINE HELP PROPERTIES, DBLCLDKEDIT, MATCHPROP

Working with Saved Layer Settings

Saving and reusing layer settings can expedite the drawing and editing process. This is especially true if you are working with complex drawings that have a large number of layers.

You can name and save groups of layer settings, called layer states, in drawings. After making changes, you can easily restore all of these settings at one time. For example, you might want to restore the settings you need to use for plotting after a heavy editing session. You can also export saved layer states, which can be imported into other drawings. This can help you avoid tedious layer setup and provide a means for making quick modifications to drawings.

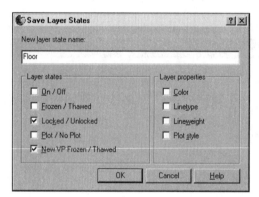

Saving Layer States

When you save a layer state, you can select any or all of these layer settings:

- ***States***: Whether a layer is on or off, frozen or thawed, locked or unlocked, and plotted or not plotted and whether the layer is frozen automatically in new viewports
- ***Properties***: Color, linetype, lineweight, and plot style

The current value of each layer setting is saved for every layer in the drawing. However, you can restore only the values of the settings you selected when you saved or edited the layer state. You edit a saved layer state by selecting different settings. Editing determines which settings are selected and restored, not their values.

For each group of layer settings you save, you specify a layer state name. You can save many named layer states in each drawing. Each saved layer state can include different settings and different values.

To help manage your work, you can rename or delete saved layer states.

Restoring Layer States

You restore a layer state by selecting the layer state name. Restoring a layer state resets the values of the drawing's layer settings to the state they were in when the layer state was saved. Only the settings that were selected when the layer state was saved or edited are affected. Layer settings that were not selected are ignored. For example, if you selected only Color and Linetype when saving a layer state, only layer-related color and linetype properties change when you restore that layer state. Also, layers that were added to the drawing after the layer state was saved are not affected.

Exporting and Importing Layer States

When you export a saved layer state, a layer state file (LAS) is created. Importing one of these files adds the saved layer state to the recipient drawing, including all of the layers and their settings from the original drawing. However, you must restore a saved layer state after importing it to ensure that its settings are applied to the recipient drawing.

During the import process, new layers might automatically be created in the recipient drawing to match the layers exported from the originating drawing.

NOTE The saved layer states of referenced drawings (xrefs) are not accessible from the current drawing. For information about xrefs, see page 230.

To get started		
Action	**Menu**	**Toolbar**
Saving, Restoring, Exporting, and Importing Layer States	Format ➤ Layer	Object Properties

ONLINE HELP LAYER

Using Editing Aids

The following editing aids help you modify drawings efficiently:

- *Use grips* to edit objects using a shortcut menu.
- *Explode compound objects* to edit their constituent objects separately.
- *Draw revision clouds* to identify areas that have been updated.
- *Group objects* to make object selection easier.

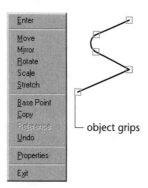

object grips

Editing with Grips

Grips are small squares that appear on an object after it has been selected. They mark control locations and are powerful editing tools. After you select an object, you can select a grip and right-click to display a short-cut menu. Then choose an editing command from the menu.

Grips are turned on in AutoCAD LT by default. You turn off grips using the Options dialog box.

Exploding Objects

Exploding an object converts it from a single object to its constituent parts. For example, exploding polylines forms simple lines and arcs. Other items that you can explode include block references, dimensions, and hatches. Exploding a block reference replaces it with copies of the objects that compose the block. Exploding dimensions and hatches replaces them with individual objects such as lines, text, points, and two-dimensional solids.

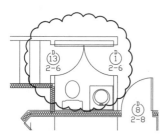

Creating Revision Clouds

If you review or redline drawings, you can increase your productivity by using revision clouds to highlight your markups. You draw the revision cloud around the objects you want to emphasize, creating a polyline of sequential arcs in the shape of a cloud, as shown in the illustration.

Grouping Objects to Streamline Selection

Use groups when you need to manipulate the same set of objects repeatedly or when you need to duplicate a set of objects in several locations within a drawing. There are two ways to create groups:

- *Unnamed groups*. Select the objects you want to group and then choose Group from the menu or toolbar. AutoCAD LT assigns a default name.
- *Named groups*. Select the objects you want to group, and use the Group Manager to assign a name and description to the group as you create it.

You can use the Group Manager to manage, as well as create, groups. You can rename groups, add and delete objects from groups, and ungroup objects.

NOTE You can combine a set of objects into a single object known as a block. Blocks are often used as symbols in drawings. For information, see page 186.

To get started			
Action	Menu	Toolbar	Dialog box tab
Enabling grips	Tools ➤ Options		Selection
Working with groups	Tools ➤ Group Tools ➤ Ungroup Tools ➤ Group Manager	Group	
Exploding objects	Modify ➤ Explode		
Creating revision clouds	Tools ➤ Revision Cloud	Draw	

ONLINE HELP OPTIONS, GROUP, EXPLODE, REVCLOUD

Analyzing Drawings

You can extract information from your model using the inquiry commands:

- DIST provides distance and angle information regarding two points.
- AREA displays the area and perimeter of objects or of a sequence of points.
- LIST displays object properties.
- ID provides the visual location of a point whose coordinate values you specify.
- TIME displays the time spent in the drawing.

Calculating Distance and Angle

Use DIST to quickly determine the relationship between two points. You can display the following information for two points you specify:

- Distance between them in drawing units
- Angle between the points in the XY plane
- Angle of the points from the XY plane
- Delta, or difference, between the X, Y, and Z coordinate values of each point

Calculating Areas

You can calculate area for open and closed objects, or you can specify points to define the area.

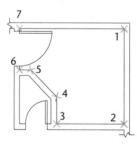

Points specified

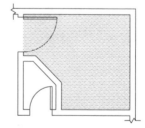

Specified area

To measure more than one area, either specify points or select objects. For example, you can measure the total area of rooms in a floor plan. You can also subtract one or more areas from a combined area. In the following example, the area of the floor plan is first measured and then a room is subtracted.

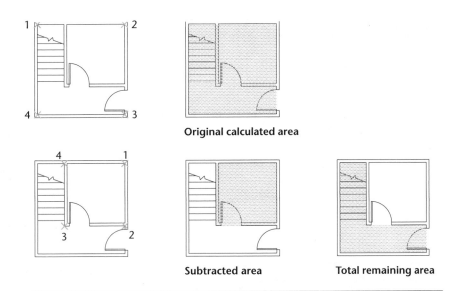

Original calculated area

Subtracted area   **Total remaining area**

NOTE One easy way to measure a closed, complex area is to use BOUNDARY to create a region or polyline defining the area. Then open the Properties window to see the area and perimeter. For more information, see page 148 and page 136.

To get started		
Action	**Menu**	**Toolbar**
Making inquiries	Tools ➤ Inquiry	Inquiry

ONLINE HELP AREA, DIST, ID, LIST, TIME

Purging Unneeded Information

Purging unneeded, unused components reduces drawing size. It is particularly helpful when you are working on large files.

Accumulating Unneeded Items

Over time, drawings may accumulate many named objects that are no longer needed. For example, you may have a text style that is no longer used or a layer that contains no drawing objects. The definitions of these unneeded items remain associated with your drawing in a virtual storage space known as the *definition tables*. They continue to require memory and other resources until you purge them. Similarly, if you insert a symbol, or *block,* into your drawing and later delete that block, the block definition remains in your drawing file until you purge it.

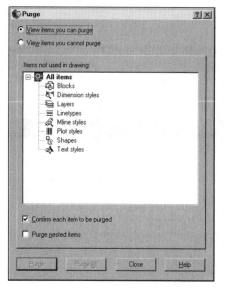

Permanently Removing Items

Since purging permanently removes items from the drawing file, be careful not to purge items you intend to use later. Otherwise, you will need to re-create them.

Purging removes only one level of information at a time. For example, if purging a layer removes the only reference to a linetype, the linetype is not removed until you purge it specifically.

Identifying Items to Purge

In the View Items You Can Purge view in the Purge dialog box, you can select items that have been deleted and are available for purging. To purge an unused named object, navigate to an individual object type and highlight it, or select All Items to purge all unused named objects.

Purging Nested Items

Purge nested items to remove *nested blocks* that have been inserted in your drawing. A nested block is contained in another block definition. Other nested items that you can purge include layers and linetypes.

Identifying Items You Cannot Purge

You can use the View Items You Cannot Purge view of the Purge dialog box to learn why an item cannot be purged. When you select an item, the reason it cannot be purged is displayed in the bottom panel of the dialog box.

Keep in mind that you cannot purge named objects, such as linetypes, that are referenced by drawing objects. Also, you cannot purge items that are default objects, such as the CONTINUOUS linetype.

To get started	
Action	**Menu**
Purging unneeded information	File ➤ Drawing Utilities ➤ Purge

ONLINE HELP PURGE

These symbols are blocks that represent standard items such as trees or bushes.

Create blocks when you want to use drawings or parts of drawings repeatedly.

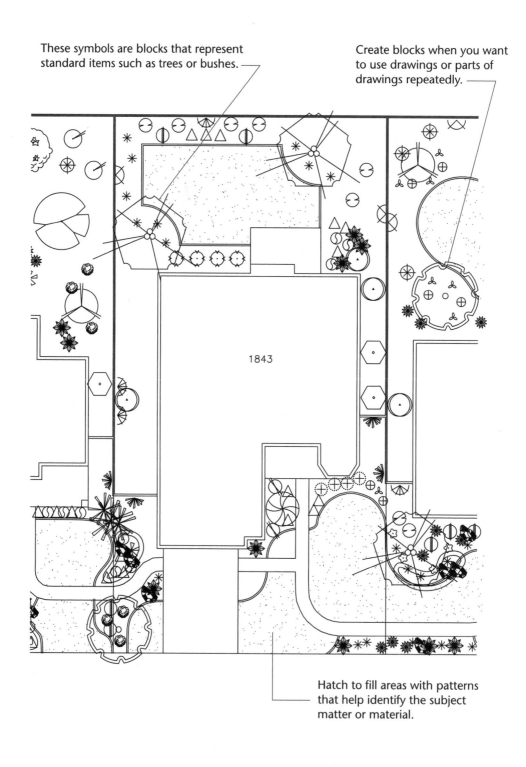

1843

Hatch to fill areas with patterns that help identify the subject matter or material.

Using Blocks, or Symbols, and Hatches Repeatedly

10

AutoCAD LT®provides several features to help you reuse objects and information repeatedly in your drawings. Using blocks, or symbols, you can organize and manipulate several objects as one component. By adding attributes, you can associate information with the blocks in your drawings. Hatching fills specified areas in a drawing with standard patterns that help identify objects.

In this chapter

- Block, or Symbol, and Hatch Overview
- Working with Blocks
- Controlling Object Properties in Blocks
- Working with Attributes
- Working with Hatches

Block, or Symbol, and Hatch Overview

Most engineering and architectural drawings contain repetitive objects and information.

- *A block* is a named collection of objects you can associate to form a single object, or *block definition*, in AutoCAD LT.
- *A hatch pattern* is a standard pattern of lines or dots used to highlight an area in a drawing, or to identify a material such as concrete or grass.

References to block definitions and hatch patterns are saved in *definition tables* that are part of the drawing where they are used.

Using Blocks

Using blocks in AutoCAD LT makes it easier and faster to get your work done.

- *Build a standard library* of frequently used symbols, components, or standard parts; you can insert the same block numerous times instead of re-creating the drawing elements each time.
- *Revise drawings efficiently* by inserting, relocating, and copying blocks rather than individual geometric objects.
- *Save disk space* by storing all references to the same block as one block definition.
- *Associate data* by including a description when you create a block.

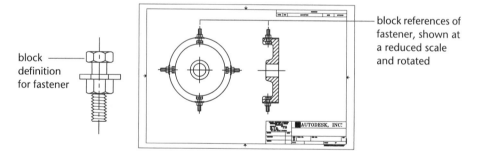

block definition for fastener

block references of fastener, shown at a reduced scale and rotated

Using Symbols

A symbol is a block that is used as an icon for a physical object such as a tree, a diode, or a table. Symbols are predefined for rapid insertion in drawings. AutoCAD LT provides some standard symbols that you can easily locate using the AutoCAD LT Today window. You can load symbols from the Today window into AutoCAD DesignCenter. Autodesk also offers a symbols product that includes symbols for architectural, mechanical, and electrical drawings. There are several other commercially available symbol libraries.

Working with Hatches

AutoCAD LT supplies a solid fill and more than 50 industry-standard hatch patterns. In addition, AutoCAD LT supplies 14 hatch patterns that conform to the ISO (International Standardization Organization) standards. You can use a pattern supplied with AutoCAD LT or one from an external pattern library. You can also create your own hatch patterns.

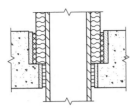

Industry-standard hatch patterns

Managing Blocks, Symbols, and Hatches

To work efficiently, you need to manage the blocks, symbols, and hatches you use. You can use DesignCenter to manage blocks, symbols, and hatches and drag them into your drawings. Blocks are often stored in *block libraries*, also called *symbol libraries*, which are drawing files that are devoted to block definitions. For information about using DesignCenter, see page 232.

NOTE Another way to create a named set of objects is to group them. With groups, you can edit, copy, or move more than one object at a time. For information about creating groups, see page 178. You can also reuse entire drawings by creating external references, or *xrefs*. For information, see page 230.

Working with Blocks

Once created, blocks consist of either definitions or references.

- *Block definitions* are created in the current drawing when you define a block. When you place the block in other drawings, you also create block definitions in the other drawings.
- *Block references* are references to a block definition that are created when you place the block in a drawing—either in the drawing where the block was created or in another drawing.

You can explode a block into its component objects, modify them, and redefine the block. The results of redefinition vary depending on where the block was originally defined and where the block reference is inserted. If you modify a block definition, all references to it in the current drawing are updated automatically. Changing the original block definition after inserting the block in a second drawing has no effect on the block reference in the second drawing. If you want changes to be reflected in the second drawing, insert an external reference instead of a block. For more information, see page 230.

Creating Block Definitions

To create a block definition, you specify a block's insertion base point (1) and then select all the objects to be included in the block definition (2 and 3). You can choose to delete the objects used to create the block from the drawing.

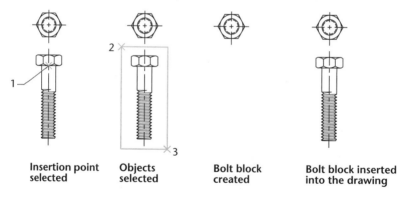

| Insertion point selected | Objects selected | Bolt block created | Bolt block inserted into the drawing |

Block definitions that contain other blocks are called *nested blocks*.

Inserting Blocks

AutoCAD LT provides three methods for inserting blocks into drawings:

- *Use DesignCenter* to share many drawing components, including block definitions.
- *Use AutoCAD LT Today* to locate symbol libraries. You can then load these symbol libraries into DesignCenter.
- *Use the Insert dialog box* to specify the insertion point, scale, and rotation angle for the block. You can also explode the resulting block reference into its component objects when you insert the block.

NOTE You can insert an entire drawing as a block into the current drawing. Doing so creates a block definition and a block reference in the current drawing.

To get started		
Action	Menu	Toolbar
Defining blocks	Draw ➤ Block ➤ Make	Draw
Inserting blocks	Insert ➤ Block	Draw
Exploding blocks	Modify ➤ Explode	Modify

ONLINE HELP BLOCK, INSERT, EXPLODE, ADCENTER, TODAY,

Controlling Object Properties in Blocks

A block can be composed of objects drawn on several layers with various colors, linetypes, and lineweights. Although you always insert a block on the current layer, you have choices for how the color, linetype, and lineweight properties of objects are treated when you insert a block reference:

- *Objects in the block retain their original properties.* The color, linetype, and lineweight properties of objects in the inserted block do not change.
- *Objects in the block inherit properties from the current layer.* Color, linetype, and lineweight properties of objects in the inserted block change to reflect the properties assigned to the current layer.
- *Objects first accept individual settings and then inherit properties from the current layer.* Color, linetype, and lineweight properties in the inserted block reflect properties you specifically assign to individual objects. Properties that are not set individually are inherited from the current layer.

Nested blocks can also inherit properties from the current layer. Keeping track of the color and line properties of nested blocks can be complicated.

Creating Objects That Retain Original Properties

The objects within an inserted block can keep their original color, linetype, and lineweight properties. For this result, create the objects that will be included in the block on any layer except 0 and set properties to anything except BYBLOCK or BYLAYER. When you insert the block in a drawing, the objects in the block appear on the layers where they were originally drawn. Layers are created in the current drawing that correspond with layers in the block.

Creating Objects That Inherit Current Layer Properties

The objects within an inserted block can inherit color, linetype, and line-weight properties from the layer they are inserted on. For this result, create the objects on layer 0. Then set the color, linetype, and lineweight for the objects to be included in the block definition to BYLAYER.

Creating Objects That Inherit Individual Settings and Then Current Layer Properties

The objects within an inserted block can change to reflect the values you have specifically set—that is, values that you have set to override the color, linetype, or lineweight assigned to the current layer. If you have not specifically set the color, linetype, or lineweight, then these properties are inherited from the current layer. For this result, create the objects on any layer and set the current color, linetype, or lineweight to BYBLOCK.

If you are inserting a block in a drawing		
And you want the objects in a block to	Create objects on these layers	Create objects with these properties
Retain original properties	Any but 0 (zero)	Any but BYBLOCK or BYLAYER
Inherit properties from the current layer	0 (zero)	BYLAYER
Inherit individual properties first, then layer properties	Any	BYBLOCK

For more information about setting object properties, see page 136.

To get started		
Action	Menu	Toolbar
Setting color, linetype, and lineweight	Tools ➤ Properties Format ➤ Layer	Object Properties
Setting the current layer	Format ➤ Layer	Object Properties

ONLINE HELP BLOCK, COLOR, LAYER, LINETYPE, LWEIGHT

Working with Attributes

An *attribute* provides a label, or *tag,* you use to attach text or numeric data to a block. You can associate more than one attribute with a block, provided that each attribute has a different tag. An attribute can be invisible, which means the attribute is not displayed or plotted. However, attribute information is stored in the drawing file. You can extract attribute information and use it to produce items such as a parts list or a bill of materials.

Blocks can have two kinds of attributes attached to them:

- *Variable attributes.* When you insert a block that has a variable attribute, AutoCAD LT prompts you to enter the data to be stored with the block. Examples of data include part number, price, and manufacturer.
- *Constant attributes.* Because constant attributes have the same value in every occurrence of the block, you are not prompted for a value.

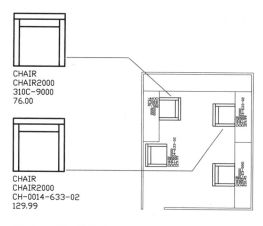

CHAIR
CHAIR2000
310C-9000
76.00

CHAIR
CHAIR2000
CH-0014-633-02
129.99

Blocks with attributes

Creating Attributes

Creating attributes involves two steps:

- Creating the attribute definition
- Including one or more attributes in a block when you define the block

To create the attribute definition, you specify the insertion point and set options that define whether the attribute is visible or invisible, variable or constant. You then enter a tag and a prompt. The tag identifies the type of information you are storing, for example, the model for a chair. When the block is inserted, the prompt requests you enter the information to be stored, for example, the model number for a particular chair.

To include the attribute in a block, you select the attribute definition and other objects when you create the block definition. To use several attributes together, define them separately and include them in the same block.

Extracting Attribute Information

You can extract attribute information from a drawing file and create a separate text file for use with database or spreadsheet applications. You must first create an attribute template file so AutoCAD LT can generate a query report containing the extracted attribute information. The template file specifies the content and sequence of the report. You use a text editor such as Notepad to create the template file.

After you create the template file, AutoCAD LT uses that file to determine what attribute information to extract from the drawing. Each field in the template file extracts information from the drawing.

To get started		
Action	**Menu**	**Toolbar**
Creating attribute definitions	Draw ➤ Block ➤ Define Attributes	
Editing an attribute definition before association with a block	Modify ➤ Object ➤ Text	Modify II
Editing an attribute definition already attached to a block	Modify ➤ Object ➤ Attribute ➤ Single	Modify II

ONLINE HELP ATTDEF, ATTEDIT, ATTEXT

Working with Hatches

Hatching fills a specified area in a drawing with a pattern or solid fill. Most hatches are *associative*. Associative hatches are linked to their boundaries and update when the boundaries are modified. You can remove associativity from a hatch at any time.

Hatched object   **Result of editing boundary with nonassociative hatch**   **Result of editing boundary with associative hatch**

You can use one of the many hatch patterns supplied in AutoCAD LT, create your own hatch pattern, or use a custom hatch pattern from another source.

Inserting Hatches

You can hatch objects in a drawing using one of these methods:

- *Choosing Hatch from the menu or toolbar* creates associative (the default) or nonassociative hatches.
- *Using DesignCenter*, you can drag associative hatches into the drawing.

Using the Hatch command from the menu or toolbar defines boundaries automatically when you specify a point within a closed area. The boundary can have *islands* (enclosed areas within the hatch area) that you choose to hatch or leave unhatched. You can also define a boundary by selecting objects.

To define a nonassociative hatch that is independent of a closed area, enter **hatch** on the command line.

Defining Hatch Boundaries

Boundaries can be any combination of objects such as lines, arcs, circles, 2D polylines, blocks, and layout viewports. By default, AutoCAD LT defines the boundary by analyzing all the closed objects in the current view. Normally, islands remain unhatched and islands within islands are hatched.

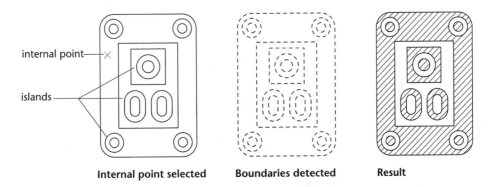

internal point

islands

Internal point selected   **Boundaries detected**   **Result**

You can remove islands so the object is completely hatched. You can also specify points to define a *boundary set* that limits the area that is hatched.

To get started		
Action	**Menu**	**Toolbar**
Hatching areas	Draw ➤ Hatch Tools ➤ AutoCAD DesignCenter	Draw Standard

ONLINE HELP   BHATCH, HATCH, FILLMODE, ADCENTER

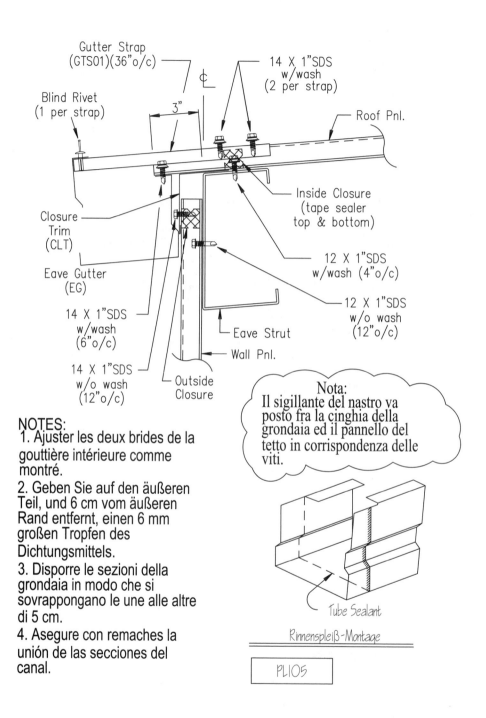

Gutter Strap
(GTS01)(36"o/c)

14 X 1"SDS
w/wash
(2 per strap)

Blind Rivet
(1 per strap)

3"

Roof Pnl.

Inside Closure
(tape sealer
top & bottom)

Closure
Trim
(CLT)

Eave Gutter
(EG)

12 X 1"SDS
w/wash (4"o/c)

14 X 1"SDS
w/wash
(6"o/c)

12 X 1"SDS
w/o wash
(12"o/c)

Eave Strut

Wall Pnl.

14 X 1"SDS
w/o wash
(12"o/c)

Outside
Closure

Nota:
Il sigillante del nastro va
posto fra la cinghia della
grondaia ed il pannello del
tetto in corrispondenza delle
viti.

NOTES:
1. Ajuster les deux brides de la
gouttière intérieure comme
montré.
2. Geben Sie auf den äußeren
Teil, und 6 cm vom äußeren
Rand entfernt, einen 6 mm
großen Tropfen des
Dichtungsmittels.
3. Disporre le sezioni della
grondaia in modo che si
sovrappongano le une alle altre
di 5 cm.
4. Asegure con remaches la
unión de las secciones del
canal.

Tube Sealant

Rinnenspleiß-Montage

PLI05

Examples of text styles you can use to annotate drawings

Adding Text

11

Text conveys important information in your drawing. You use text for title blocks and to label parts of the drawing, to give specifications, or to make annotations.

AutoCAD LT® provides various ways to create text. Although all text you enter uses the current text style, which establishes the default font and format settings, you can use several methods to change text appearance.

For information about adding leader lines with annotation to your drawings, see page 214.

In this chapter

- Creating and Modifying Text
- Working with Text Styles
- Checking Spelling
- Finding and Replacing Text

Creating and Modifying Text

AutoCAD LT provides two methods for adding text to drawings, one for short entries such as labels and one for longer, more complex entries.

- *Single-line text* ends a line each time you press ENTER.
- *Multiline text* fits a specified width but can extend vertically to an indefinite length. It is sometimes called paragraph text.

You can assign the same styles to both types of text. However, you can apply formats to individual words and characters only with multiline text.

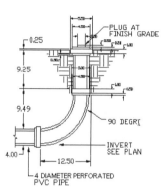

Each row of single-line text is a separate object

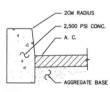

Entire paragraph of multiline text is a single object

Working with Single-Line Text

To create single-line text, you specify an insertion point for the first character. You may also specify text style, a rotation angle, an alignment option, and a text height. After typing, you press ENTER to end the line and create a text object.

Like any other object, a single-line text object can be moved, rotated, erased, and copied. You also can mirror, or make a reverse copy of, text.

The limited formatting capabilities available with single-line text include underlining.

Working with Multiline Text

You can create multiline text using:

- The Multiline Text Editor
- The command line
- An alternative text editor

The Multiline Text Editor provides a quick way to set properties that affect the entire text object and formats that affect only selected text. You can also control line spacing in this dialog box.

Choose the font and text height.

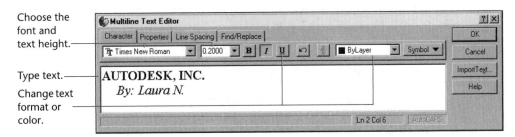

Type text.

Change text format or color.

Before creating the text, you define the paragraph's width by specifying the two opposite corners of a text boundary. AutoCAD LT inserts the text you enter in the dialog box within this limit and wraps words that don't fit to the next line. You can apply the text height, justification, rotation angle, and style to the text object and apply character formatting to selected characters. Later, you can move, rotate, erase, copy, mirror, stretch, or scale the text.

For information about using imported text in drawings, see page 234.

To get started		
Action	**Menu**	**Toolbar**
Creating single-line text	Draw ➤ Single Line Text	
Creating multiline text	Draw ➤ Paragraph Text	Draw
Modifying text	Modify ➤ Object ➤ Text	Modify II

ONLINE HELP TEXT, MTEXT, DDEDIT, MIRRTEXT, MTEXTED

Working with Text Styles

All text in an AutoCAD LT drawing has a text *style* associated with it. When you enter text, AutoCAD LT uses the current text style, which determines

- **Font.** The shapes of the text characters
- **Font style.** Italic and boldface formatting for TrueType fonts
- **Height.** The size in drawing units of the font you use
- **Obliquing angle.** The forward or backward slant of the text
- **Orientation.** The vertical or horizontal alignment of single-line text
- **Other text characteristics.** Effects such as wide text, upside down, and backwards text

Creating and Modifying Text Styles

Except for the default STANDARD style, you must define any text style that you want to use. Once you've created a style, you can modify its settings, change its name, or delete it when you no longer need it. When you create or modify a text style, you use the Text Style dialog box.

To use a different style, select a different style name.

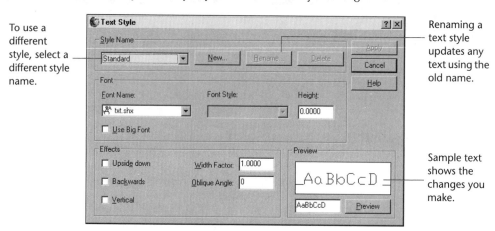

Renaming a text style updates any text using the old name.

Sample text shows the changes you make.

New styles inherit settings from the current text style, unless you change them. If you change an existing style's font or orientation, all text using that style is regenerated using the new font or orientation. Changing text height does not change existing text but does change subsequently created text objects. Changes to alignment, width, and rotation affect only single-line text; they have no effect on multiline text.

Setting Font and Obliquing Angle

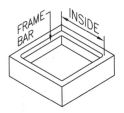

You can assign a font to a text style by selecting a TrueType typeface name and its font style (bold, for instance) or an AutoCAD LT SHX font. You can create several similar styles based on a standard font. The example shows the same font used by different styles with different obliquing settings. The obliquing angle represents the offset from 90 degrees. A value between –85 and 85 makes the text oblique. A positive obliquing angle slants text to the right. A negative angle slants it to the left.

Setting Text Height

The text height you set should be determined by the scale factor of your drawing. You can create different text styles for different scale factors and layouts. You are prompted for the text height every time you create text if you leave the text height at 0 (zero). For more information about scaling, see page 98 and page 244.

To get started	
Action	**Menu**
Creating text styles	Format ➤ Text Style

ONLINE HELP STYLE

Checking Spelling

You can check the spelling in your drawing, including spelling in dimension text, using one of several *main dictionaries*, available in different languages. The main dictionaries use a standard word list, which you can customize.

During a spelling check, AutoCAD LT matches the words in the drawing to the words in the current main dictionary. Any words you add are stored in the custom dictionary that is current at the time of the spelling check. For example, you can add proper names so that AutoCAD LT no longer identifies them as misspelled words.

Correcting Misspellings

When you check spelling, you select the objects you want to check or enter **all** on the command line to select all text objects. If AutoCAD LT does not find any misspelled words, it displays a message. If AutoCAD LT finds a questionable word, it displays the Check Spelling dialog box. You use this dialog box to correct misspellings and to change dictionaries. To check spelling in another language, you can change to a different main dictionary.

Select the suggested word from the list, and then choose Change to apply it.

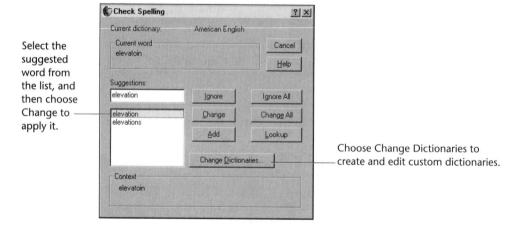

Choose Change Dictionaries to create and edit custom dictionaries.

Creating and Editing Custom Dictionaries

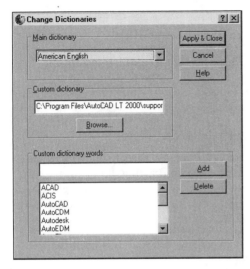

You can create *custom dictionaries* and switch to them as needed. A custom dictionary is a list of spelling exceptions that you have identified. Custom dictionaries all use the *.cus* file extension. You can use any ASCII text editor to add and delete words in one of these files or to combine dictionaries. If a word in the dictionary is preceded by a tilde (~), AutoCAD LT always flags that word as incorrect.

You can also create, edit, and set alternative custom dictionaries from inside AutoCAD LT using the Change Dictionaries option in the Check Spelling dialog box. To create a new custom dictionary, you enter a new name under Custom Dictionary in the Change Dictionaries dialog box.

To get started		
Action	Menu	Toolbar
Checking spelling	Tools ➤ Spelling	Standard

ONLINE HELP   SPELL, DCTCUST, DCTMAIN

Finding and Replacing Text

You can quickly find and replace text using two methods in AutoCAD LT. Both methods can find whole words only and match case.

- **Find and Replace** works with single-line text, multiline text, block attributes, dimension annotations, and hyperlinks.
- **MultiLine Text Editor** finds or replaces multiline text in the Multiline Text Editor only.

Searching an Entire Drawing File for Text

The Find and Replace dialog box can find, replace, select, and zoom to text found in numerous locations throughout your drawing. It can find text in model space as well as in any layout defined in the current drawing. You can limit the search to a specific selection set or search the entire drawing. However, you cannot find text within block references.

Enter the text to find. ⎯⎯⎯⎯

Enter the words to replace the found text.

Choose to search the entire drawing or a selection set.

Choose to set limits for the search.

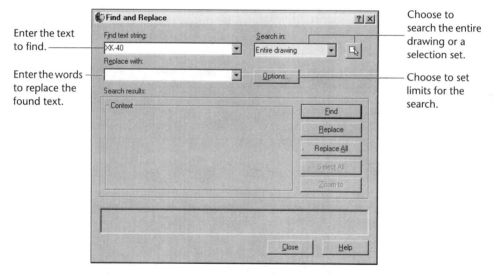

In your search criteria, you can indicate which types of text to find. For example, you may need to find the junction box block with the attribute value XK-40 because it needs maintenance. You can easily find and zoom to the block with this specific attribute value using the Find and Replace dialog box.

Finding and Replacing Multiline Text

To quickly search for and replace text in an individual multiline text object, use the Find and Replace tab in the Multiline Text Editor. You can replace text content only, not character formatting or text properties.

In the Find box, enter the text to change.

In the Replace With box, enter the replacement text.

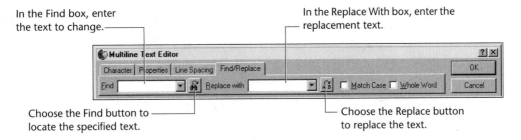

Choose the Find button to locate the specified text.

Choose the Replace button to replace the text.

NOTE To access the Find and Replace dialog box using a shortcut menu, end any active commands and right-click in the graphics area.

To get started		
Action	**Menu**	**Toolbar**
Finding and replacing text	Edit ➤ Find Draw ➤ Text Modify ➤ Object ➤ Text	Draw

ONLINE HELP FIND, MTEXT, DDEDIT

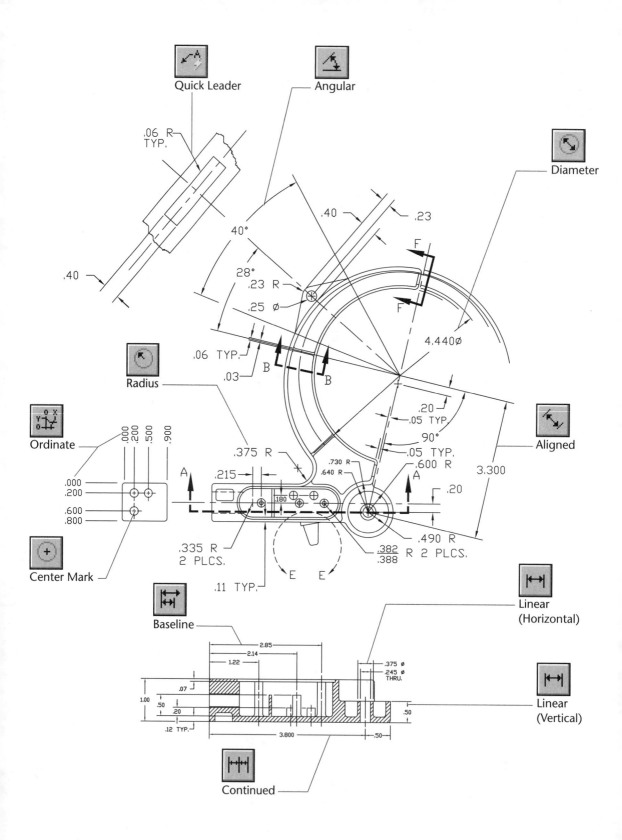

Quick Leader

Angular

Diameter

.06 R
TYP.

.40

40°

28°

.23 R

.25 ⌀

.40

.23

F

F

4.440⌀

Radius

.06 TYP.

.03

B

B

.20

.05 TYP.

90°

.05 TYP.

Aligned

Ordinate

.000
.200
.500
.900

.000
.200

.600
.800

A

.215

.375 R

.180

.730 R
.640 R

A

.600 R

.20

3.300

Center Mark

.335 R
2 PLCS.

.11 TYP.

E

E

.382
.388

.490 R

R 2 PLCS.

Baseline

2.85

2.14

1.22

.07

1.00

.50

.20

.12 TYP.

3.800

.375 ⌀
.245 ⌀
THRU.

.50

.50

Linear
(Horizontal)

Linear
(Vertical)

Continued

Dimensioning

12

Dimensions are a key component of precision drawings. They show the exact measurements required to re-create the model you draw. Dimensioning options such as leader lines with annotation, tolerances, and centerlines provide additional information. Dimension styles help you enforce formatting standards.

In this chapter

- Dimensioning Overview
- Creating Dimensions
- Getting Started with Dimensions
- Using Dimensioning Options
- Creating and Modifying Dimension Styles
- Modifying Dimensions

Dimensioning Overview

Dimensions show the geometric measurements of objects, the distances or angles between objects, or the location of a feature. AutoCAD LT® offers four types of dimensions:

- **Linear.** Measures distances using horizontal, vertical, aligned, rotated, baseline (parallel), and continued (chain) dimensions.
- **Ordinate.** Measures the distance of a point from a specified origin point.
- **Radial.** Measures the radii and diameters of arcs and circles.
- **Angular.** Measures the angle formed by two lines or three points.

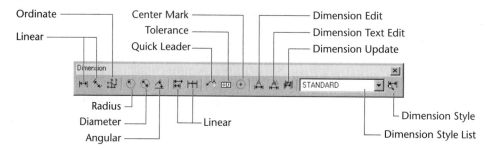

Every dimension has a *dimension style* associated with it, whether it is the default or one you define. The style controls characteristics such as color, text style, and dimension scale. *Secondary styles* allow for subtle modifications to a base style for different types of dimensions. *Overrides* allow for style modifications to a specific dimension.

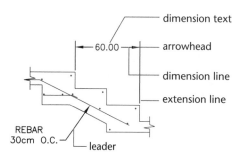

Parts of a Dimension

Dimensions have several distinct elements:

- **Dimension line.** Indicates the direction and extent of a dimension. For angles, the dimension line is an arc.
- **Extension lines.** Extend from the feature being dimensioned to the dimension line; also called projection lines or witness lines.
- **Dimension text.** Reflects dimension value and may include prefixes, suffixes, and tolerances. Alternatively, you can supply your own text or suppress the text entirely.
- **Arrowheads.** Indicates an end of the dimension line; can be suppressed.

- *Leaders*. Form a solid line leading from an annotation to the referenced feature. AutoCAD LT creates some leaders automatically when dimension text won't fit between extension lines. You may also create *leader lines* to connect text or a block with a feature.

Associative Dimensions and Leaders

By default, AutoCAD LT creates *associative* dimensions. Associative dimensions are dimensions in which all the lines, arrowheads, arcs, and text are drawn as a single dimension object. As a result, you can update a dimension automatically as you modify the object with which it is associated. You can create nonassociative dimensions if you need greater flexibility in controlling their appearance. In general, however, the ability to modify each dimension as a single object makes associative dimensions easier to maintain.

Leader lines are associated with the annotation—that is, when the annotation is relocated, the leader is updated accordingly.

NOTE Arrowheads are available in several types, including architectural ticks and dots.

Creating Dimensions

You can dimension lines, double lines, arcs, circles, and polyline segments. Or you can draw dimensions that stand alone by specifying points on separate objects to measure the distance between them. AutoCAD LT draws dimensions on the current layer. There are two primary methods for creating dimensions:

- Select an object to dimension (1) and specify the dimension line location (2) as shown in the following examples.
- Use object snaps to specify the extension line origins, and then specify the dimension line location.

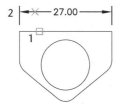

Result of selecting a line to dimension

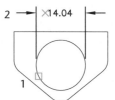

Result of selecting a circle to dimension

Creating Linear and Aligned Dimensions

As you create linear dimensions, you can modify the text, the angle of the text, or the angle of the dimension line. AutoCAD LT automatically applies a horizontal or vertical dimension, depending on the extension line origins you specify or the point where you select an object. However, you can specify horizontal or vertical when you create the dimension. Aligned dimensions are also linear dimensions, but they place the dimension line parallel to the line connecting the dimension's definition points, regardless of angle.

Creating Radial Dimensions

Radial dimensions include radius and diameter measurement. They are associated with a centerline or center mark if you place the dimension line outside the circle or arc.

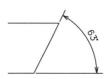

Creating Angular Dimensions

To dimension an angle, specify the angle vertex and endpoints. To dimension the angle between two lines, select the lines and specify the location of the dimension line arc.

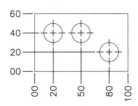

Ordinate dimensions

Creating Ordinate Dimensions

Ordinate dimensions measure the distance from an origin point, called the datum, to a feature, such as a hole in a part. Ordinate dimensions consist of an X or Y ordinate with a leader line. The X-datum measures the distance along the X axis. The Y-datum measures the distance along the Y axis.

Creating Baseline and Continued Dimensions

Baseline dimensions are multiple dimensions measured from the *same* baseline. Continued dimensions are multiple dimensions placed end to end that use the origin of each dimension's *second* extension line as the origin for the next dimension's *first* extension line. You must create a linear, ordinate, or angular dimension before you create baseline or continued dimensions.

To get started		
Action	**Menu**	**Toolbar**
Creating dimensions	See the next topic	See the next topic

ONLINE HELP DIMALIGNED, DIMANGULAR, DIMCEN, DIMCONTINUE, DIMDIAMETER, DINLINEAR, DIMORDINATE, DIMRADIUS, DIMBASELINE

Getting Started with Dimensions

The following table illustrates the available dimension types and shows how to get started creating them.

To get started		
Action	**Menu**	**Toolbar**
Creating linear dimensions horizontal vertical	Dimension ➤ Linear	
Creating aligned dimensions	Dimension ➤ Aligned	
Creating ordinate dimensions	Dimension ➤ Ordinate	
Creating radius dimensions	Dimension ➤ Radius	
Creating diameter dimensions	Dimension ➤ Diameter	

To get started (continued)

Action	Menu	Toolbar
Creating angular dimensions	Dimension ➤ Angular	
Creating baseline dimensions	Dimension ➤ Baseline	
Creating continued dimensions	Dimension ➤ Continue	

Using Dimensioning Options

In addition to the basic types of dimensions, AutoCAD LT provides these options on the Dimension menu and toolbar:

- **Center marks and centerlines** locate the exact center of circles or arcs.
- **Leader lines** connect annotation to drawing features.
- **Geometric tolerances** show deviations of form, profile, orientation, location, and runout of drawing features.

Creating Center Marks and Lines

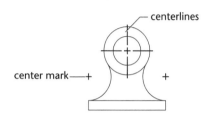

You can create a center mark or centerline on a circle or arc by using any object selection method to select the arc or circle after starting a command. You specify the size of center marks and lines when you create a dimension style. You can also create center marks with the radius and diameter dimensions.

Creating Leaders with Annotation

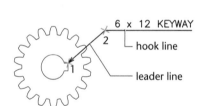

You can create a leader from any point or feature in a drawing. Leaders can be straight line segments or smooth spline curves. Leader color, scale, and arrowhead style are controlled by the current dimension style. A small line known as a *hook line* usually connects the annotation to the leader line. Leader annotations can be multiline text, a feature control frame, or a block reference.

The simple leader in the example was created by specifying the From (1) and To (2) points of the leader, pressing ENTER, and then entering the leader text.

Adding Geometric Tolerances

You use the Geometric Tolerance dialog box to add tolerances in *feature control frames*. The following example shows the parts of a feature control frame.

primary, secondary, and tertiary datum reference letters ———————————

tolerance value ————————

geometric characteristic
symbol—in this case, ————
position

$$\oplus \;\big|\; \varnothing\, 0.127\, \text{\textcircled{M}}\;\big|\; A\, \text{\textcircled{M}}\;\big|\; B\, \text{\textcircled{S}}\;\big|\; C\, \text{\textcircled{L}}$$

optional diameter symbol ————————

material conditions of tolerance ————————

material conditions of datums ————————

A feature control frame contains all the tolerance information for a single dimension and consists of at least two compartments. The first compartment contains a symbol that represents the geometric characteristic to which a tolerance is being applied, for example, form, position, or runout. The second contains the tolerance value, which may be preceded by a diameter symbol and followed by a material condition symbol, where applicable. (Material conditions apply to features that can vary in size.) The tolerance values in the feature control frame are followed by up to three optional *datum reference letters* and their modifying symbols. (A datum is a theoretically exact point, axis, or plane from which you make measurements.)

To get started

Action	Menu	Toolbar
Creating center marks	Dimension ➤ Center Mark	Dimension
Creating leaders with annotation	Dimension ➤ Leader	Dimension
Adding geometric tolerances	Dimension ➤ Tolerance	Dimension

ONLINE HELP LEADER, QLEADER, TOLERANCE, DIMCENTER

Creating and Modifying Dimension Styles

Every dimension has a *dimension style*. Dimension styles help you establish and enforce drafting standards. Styles also make changing dimension formats and behavior easy. A dimension style defines

- Format and position of dimension lines, extension lines, arrowheads, and center marks
- Appearance, position, and behavior of dimension text
- Rules governing where AutoCAD LT places text and dimension lines
- Overall dimension scale
- Format and precision of primary, alternate, and angular dimension units
- Format and precision of tolerance values

New dimensions use the current style in the Dimension Style Manager dialog box. You can also select a style from the drop-down list on the Dimension toolbar. AutoCAD LT assigns the default STANDARD style to dimensions until you set another style as current.

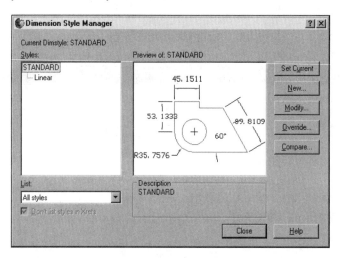

The Dimension Style Manager creates, modifies, and overrides dimension styles. You base new styles on existing styles, changing settings as appropriate. You can create *secondary styles,* variations of a single style, for each dimension type, or you can set up entirely new styles.

Modifications and overrides you make to a style in the Dimension Style Manager apply to *all* dimensions that use that style. Overrides apply to *all subsequent* dimensions created with that style until you make a new style current. They do not permanently modify a style. You can also override properties of dimensions using the Properties window. For information, see page 174.

Regardless of whether you choose New, Modify, or Override in the Dimension Style Manager, AutoCAD LT presents you with the same set of options:

- *Lines and Arrows* sets the appearance and behavior of the dimension lines, extension lines, arrowheads, center marks, and centerlines.
- *Text* sets the dimension text appearance, placement, and alignment.
- *Fit* sets options governing where AutoCAD LT places dimension lines, extension lines, and text. It also defines the overall dimension scale.
- *Primary Units* sets the format (for example, scientific, decimal, architectural) and precision of linear and angular dimension units.
- *Alternate Units* sets alternate unit format and precision.
- *Tolerances* sets tolerance values and precision.

For information about scaling dimensions, see page 98 and page 244.

To get started		
Action	Menu	Toolbar
Creating and modifying dimension styles	Dimension ➤ Style	Dimension

ONLINE HELP DIMSTYLE, DIMOVERRIDE

Modifying Dimensions

You can modify dimensions with grips or with the AutoCAD LT editing commands. You can also modify or override dimension styles, as discussed in the previous topic.

Updating Associative Dimensions While Editing Objects

When you edit dimensioned objects, you can automatically update associative dimensions. To do so, you must include the relevant dimension *definition points* in the selection set. The illustration shows that most definition points (circled) differ depending on dimension type. The middle point of dimension text is a definition point for *all* types of dimensions.

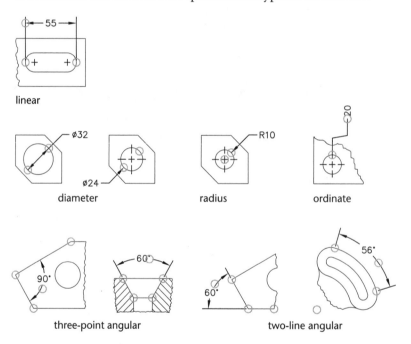

linear

diameter   radius   ordinate

three-point angular   two-line angular

Some editing commands change the definition points. For example, the definition points of a stretched or rotated dimension change because the size or shape of the object has changed. If the dimension is copied or arrayed, the definition points remain the same. The following illustration shows how to stretch the top vertex of the triangle. You must include definition points for the aligned and vertical dimensions in the crossing selection (1 and 2) so that the dimensions are stretched as well.

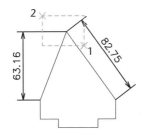 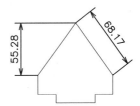

Editing Dimensions Only

You can edit dimensions, but not the associated objects, by these methods:

- *Moving dimension text outside extension lines.* Select and stretch existing dimension text, which also changes the dimension line.
- *Making extension lines oblique.* Select a dimension and change the angle.
- *Rotating dimension text.* Specify a rotation angle and then select dimensions to apply the change to.
- *Moving dimension text on the dimension line.* Select the grip in the middle of the text and drag it to a new location.

To get started		
Action	Menu	Toolbar
Making extension lines oblique	Dimension ➤ Oblique	
Moving and rotating dimension text	Dimension ➤ Align Text	Dimension

ONLINE HELP   DIMEDIT, DIMTEDIT, DIMOVERRIDE

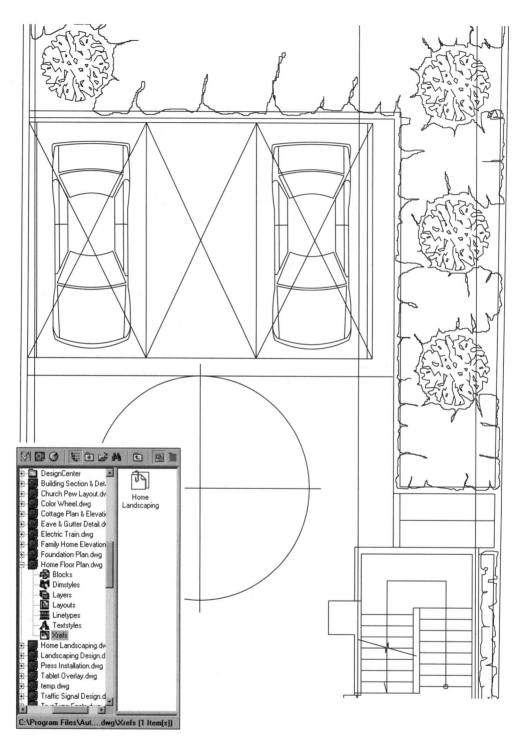

Home Floor Plan drawing with Home Landscaping drawing placed as an external reference using DesignCenter

Information Sharing

13

Reusing and sharing content is fundamental to efficient management of a drawing project. AutoCAD LT® facilitates heads-up design by providing efficient, direct ways to locate and reuse information.

Using external references, or *xrefs*, you can overlay or attach entire drawings to your current drawing. Any changes that have been made in the referenced drawing appear in the current drawing when you open it. You can easily locate, insert using drag and drop, and organize drawing content across your system and network drives—or even the Internet—using Design-Center.™ You also can use technologies such as OLE (object linking and embedding) and the World Wide Web with AutoCAD LT.

Information Sharing Overview

AutoCAD LT provides these basic mechanisms for sharing and locating information in CAD drawings:

- *Multiple-document environment.* Open and work on multiple drawings at the same time in a single AutoCAD LT session.
- *AutoCAD compatibility and export file formats.* Easily share drawings with AutoCAD users and other design professionals.
- *Custom drawing properties.* Add summary information to drawing files.

Opening Multiple Drawings

You can share information between open drawings, which helps you maintain consistency between drawings and reduces the amount of time spent redrawing similar design ideas. With multiple drawings open in a single AutoCAD LT session, you can use these features:

- *Object drag and drop.* Drag objects between open drawings.
- *Property painter.* Copy properties from objects in one open drawing to objects in another with the pointing device.
- *Cut, copy, and paste commands.* Easily transfer objects between open drawings.
- *Concurrent command execution.* Switch between open drawings without canceling the current command, and then return to the original command and complete it.

Using AutoCAD Compatibility and Export File Formats

In AutoCAD LT, you can open and view all AutoCAD files, including files from AutoCAD 2000i and earlier versions. You can edit objects in these files, including objects that cannot be created in AutoCAD LT. Sometimes the editing is limited to simple tasks such as moving, copying, and erasing.

AutoCAD LT provides options for exporting and saving files in other file formats. Most important, you can save files in several versions of the drawing interchange format (DXF) supported by AutoCAD 2000i. This industry-standard format can be read by most computer-aided design programs. You can also export drawings as Windows®metafiles (WMF) and bitmap images (BMP), and plot to encapsulated PostScript (EPS) files with AutoCAD LT.

For information about drawing Web format (DWF) files, see page 224.

Locating Files with Custom Drawing Properties

Finding the files you need facilitates information sharing. You can track your drawings more easily by assigning custom *properties* to them. The summary information you can embed in your drawing files using the Drawing Properties dialog box includes the drawing title, subject, author, keywords, and comments. You can use this information to retrieve files. You can also add keywords to drawing files, and then use DesignCenter to search for drawings using the keywords.

NOTE With DesignCenter, you can share drawing content such as blocks and text styles between drawings. For information, see page 232. You can also create external references by linking entire drawings to other drawings. For information, see page 230.

To get started

Action	Menu	Toolbar
Opening multiple drawings at once	File ➤ Open	Standard
Exporting files in WMF format Exporting files in DWF, raster, and EPS formats Exporting files in DXF format	File ➤ Export File ➤ Plot File ➤ Save As	Standard
Viewing and updating drawing properties	File ➤ Drawing Properties	

ONLINE HELP OPEN, EXPORT, DWGPROPS, BMPOUT, PSOUT

Putting Drawings on the Web

Putting files on the Internet is a quick and easy way to distribute drawings. You can make drawings available over the Web to project team members and to clients by

- *Creating attractively formatted HTML pages with drawing images* and publishing them to the Web
- *Saving drawing files to Internet or intranet locations* where others can open them or drag them from locations on Web pages, called i-drop handles, into open drawing files, automatically inserting them as blocks
- *Publishing drawing Web format (DWF) files* that can be viewed and plotted by users with Volo View or with an Internet browser and a plug-in

To view and print DWF files from an Internet browser, you can use the *WHIP!* plug-in, which is automatically included in a typical installation of AutoCAD LT 2000i. You can also view and plot DWF files using Volo View.

Creating Web Pages That Include Drawings

You can use the Publish to Web wizard to quickly and easily create Web pages that include DWF or JPG images of drawings. After selecting one of three page formats, you select one or more images to be displayed on the page. To add new images, simply use the wizard to edit the page. The wizard also helps you post the pages to an Internet or intranet location.

Opening and Saving Files from the Internet

With the Browse the Web dialog box, you can navigate quickly to an Internet location to open or save a file. Using this dialog box to access files is useful when you don't know the correct URL (Uniform Resource Locator), or when you want to avoid entering a long URL. You can browse Internet sites without having exact addresses. If you know the exact URL of a file you want to open or save, you can enter it directly in standard file selection dialog boxes or the Save Drawing As dialog box.

You can attach externally referenced drawings stored on the Internet or an intranet to drawings stored locally on your system. For example, you might have a set of construction drawings that are modified daily by contractors stored in a project directory on the Internet. You can attach the Internet drawings as xrefs to a master drawing maintained on your computer.

Using ePlot to Publish DWF Files

With the ePlot feature, you can publish electronic drawing files on the Internet. The DWF files you create support real-time panning and zooming as well as control over the display of layers and named views. Sending and receiving DWF files is faster than using DWG files, and DWF files can be viewed even without running AutoCAD LT.

As the name suggests, ePlot creates a virtual electronic plot. You can specify a variety of settings, such as pen assignments, rotation, and paper size, to control the appearance of plotted DWF files. With ePlot, you can also set

- *File resolution* to control drawing precision and minimize file size
- *File compression* to minimize file size

For more information about plotting, see page 250.

To get started		
Action	**Menu**	**Toolbar**
Creating Web pages with drawing images	File ➤ Publish to Web	Internet
Opening and saving files from the Internet	File ➤ Open File ➤ Save As	Standard
Using ePlot to publish DWF files	File ➤ Plot	Standard

ONLINE HELP PUBLISHTOWEB, OPEN, SAVEAS, PLOT

Collaborating over a Network

Networks are excellent mediums for collaborative design. You can capitalize on the Internet and your local network resources to

- *Share a single drawing session* with remote team members
- *Insert hyperlinks* in your drawings for easy access to related documents
- *Get customized Internet or intranet access* to services and information important to your design community

Using Meet Now to Share Drawing Sessions

You can share a single drawing session with up to eight other people using Meet Now. While you edit a drawing on your computer, other people can watch you work from theirs. You can perform demonstrations, hold trouble-shooting sessions—even allow others to edit your drawing—regardless of the work site for each user. The only restriction is that only one person at a time can use this technology to control the drawing session.

Working in conjunction with Microsoft NetMeeting, Meet Now provides the following supplementary features:

- A toolbar shortcut to NetMeeting and a special Help file
- Automatic meeting creation with the launch of Meet Now
- A directory server to help you locate other users

Working with Hyperlinks

You can attach *hyperlinks* to any graphical object in an AutoCAD LT drawing. Hyperlinks are pointers you create in your drawings that provide jumps to associated files. They can point to files that are stored locally, on a network drive, or on the Internet. Hyperlinks provide a simple and powerful way to quickly associate various documents with your drawings. Use hyperlinks to

- Activate a Web browser and load a particular HTML page
- Launch a word processing or spreadsheet program and open a file

Using AutoCAD LT Today to Leverage Design Resources

The AutoCAD LT Today window integrates the ability to open and save draw-ings with access to network-based resources for the design community. You can make AutoCAD LT Today a gateway to a wide range of design informa-tion and tools by setting preferences to include access to

- *A bulletin board* that provides information of interest to people in your organization. CAD managers can use this feature to communicate with design teams using local intranets. Content could include resources such as CAD standards and links to block libraries.

■ *The Autodesk Point A design portal*, which is a Web site for the AutoCAD design community. It makes resources such as online discussion groups, symbols, Autodesk Express Tools, tips and techniques, and industry-related news available all on one site. You can customize the content and presentation of information to tailor it to your interests.

To get started		
Action	**Menu**	**Toolbar**
Sharing drawing sessions	Tools ➤ Meet Now	Standard
Inserting hyperlinks in drawings	Insert ➤ Hyperlink	Standard
Using AutoCAD LT Today	Tools ➤ Today *or* Help ➤ Today	Standard
Opening the Autodesk Point A design portal outside of the Today window	Tools ➤ Autodesk Point A	Standard

ONLINE HELP MEETNOW, HYPERLINK, HYPERLINKOPTIONS, HYPERLINK-BASE, INSERT, SELECTURL, BROWSER, TODAY, OPTIONS

Working in AutoCAD Files

AutoCAD LT offers full compatibility when working with AutoCAD drawings. However, you should understand how AutoCAD LT handles features available in AutoCAD 2000i, including

- Nonrectangular layout viewports
- Multiple user coordinate systems in a single drawing file
- Saved layer settings
- 2D and 3D solid object shading

Editing Nonrectangular Layout Viewports

In AutoCAD 2000 or 2000i, you can create a layout viewport with irregular boundaries by converting an object drawn in paper space into a viewport. When you open a drawing that contains these nonrectangular viewports in AutoCAD LT, you can edit the viewports. For example, you can move, copy, or rotate a nonrectangular viewport. You can also dimension, pan, or scale the model shown in a viewport. However, you cannot create nonrectangular viewports in AutoCAD LT.

Working with Multiple User Coordinate Systems

In AutoCAD 2000 or 2000i, you can choose to use a different user coordinate system (UCS) in each viewport in a single drawing file. In AutoCAD LT, you can use only one UCS in each drawing file. The AutoCAD LT behavior is the same as it was in previous releases. For information, see page 122.

When you open an AutoCAD drawing file in AutoCAD LT, AutoCAD LT uses only the UCS from the current viewport. If you edit the drawing in AutoCAD LT, and then save it and reopen it in AutoCAD, you may notice some discrepancies in UCS usage. User coordinate systems that were set individually in AutoCAD will probably change if the viewports that use them were activated in the AutoCAD LT session.

Working with AutoCAD 2D and 3D Solid Object Shading

In AutoCAD, the SHADEMODE command provides shading and wireframe options for objects in the current viewport. Of the seven options available in AutoCAD, only two are available in AutoCAD LT: 2D Wireframe and Hidden. You can use the SHADEMODE command in AutoCAD LT to turn rendering off in viewports that were created in AutoCAD using the remaining five options. This exposes the underlying geometry so you can easily edit drawings and use the geometry with precision drawing tools such as object snaps.

WARNING! Once you use the SHADEMODE command in AutoCAD LT to turn rendering off for an object created in AutoCAD, you *cannot* turn it back on except by using the UNDO command. If you make changes to the object, you can turn the rendering on again *only* in AutoCAD.

ONLINE HELP VPORTS, LAYER, SHADEMODE

Reusing Entire Drawings with External References

An external reference, or *xref*, links another drawing to the current drawing. A drawing that is inserted as an xref in the current drawing is updated when the referenced drawing changes. Because the xref geometry is not saved in the current, or *host,* drawing, the xref does not significantly increase the file size of the host drawing. Using xrefs, you can

- Assemble a master drawing from component drawings
- Coordinate your work with the work of others by overlaying drawings
- Use object snaps to snap to precise points in a referenced drawing
- Ensure that the most recent version of the referenced drawing is displayed

Updating Xrefs

Whenever you open or plot a drawing, AutoCAD LT reloads each xref to reflect the latest state of the referenced drawing. After you make changes to an externally referenced drawing and save the file, other users can access your changes immediately by reloading the xref.

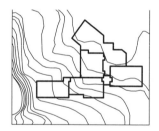 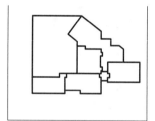 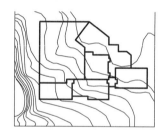

Xref attached to contour map   Xref file of site plan edited   Xref updated

Working with Xrefs

You have two choices for inserting xrefs in your drawings:

- *Attaching xrefs* helps you build drawings from other drawings. If you *nest* xrefs within other xrefs, you can see them all from the host drawing.
- *Overlaying xrefs* facilitates data sharing, but does not display nested xrefs. If you reference a drawing that itself contains an overlaid xref, the overlaid xref does not appear in the host drawing.

You can also *bind* an xref to convert it to a block and make the xref a permanent part of the drawing. Binding xrefs can be practical when a project is complete and no modifications are expected. For information about using blocks, see page 186.

Managing Xrefs

You can manage all of your externally referenced drawings in the Xref Manager. You can

- Attach a new xref
- Detach, reload, or unload an existing xref, or change the xref path
- Change an attachment to an overlay
- Bind the xref definition to the current drawing

In the Xref Manager, you can view the xrefs in either a list view or a hierarchical tree view. In list view, you see an alphabetical list of the xref definitions in the current drawing. You can sort the list by each of the columns: reference name, status, file size, xref type (attachment or overlay), file date, or saved path. The tree view displays only the relationships between xrefs, including the levels of nesting.

To get started

Action	Menu	Toolbar
Inserting external references	Tools ➤ DesignCenter Insert ➤ External Reference	Standard Insert
Managing external references	Insert ➤ Xref Manager	

ONLINE HELP XATTACH, XREF, XBIND, ADCENTER

Reusing Content with DesignCenter

DesignCenter helps you locate and manage drawing content—and insert it into your drawings. Use DesignCenter to access the following kinds of content in local, network, and Web-based files:

- Drawings as block references or xrefs
- Block definitions within drawings
- Other drawing content, such as layouts, layer definitions, layer settings, hatches, linetypes, lineweights, and dimension and text styles

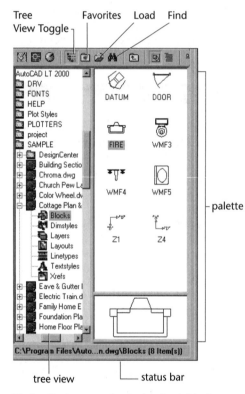

Tree View Toggle, Favorites, Load, Find, palette, tree view, status bar

DesignCenter accessing a drawing's blocks

Loading Files

You load files, including symbol libraries, into the DesignCenter palette from tree view, the Symbol Libraries tab in the AutoCAD LT Today window, the Load Palette dialog box, or the *Favorites* folder.

You can navigate to specific files using the tree view, and then select a file in tree view to load it into the palette. You can display your entire desktop hierarchy, or only the open drawing files in the tree view. The Tree View Toggle button turns the tree view on and off.

Choose Load to navigate to files on local and network drives, in the *Favorites* folder, or on the Web. In the Load Palette dialog box, you can load a file into DesignCenter. To load a file from the Web, use the Load Palette dialog box or double-click an item in *Favorites*.

Looking in Favorites

To save time loading frequently used drawings, folders, and Internet locations, choose the Favorites button. This displays the content of the *Favorites* folder, which includes shortcuts that you create for items you access often. You can add items to *Favorites* using the Load Palette dialog box.

Searching for Files

To search for files, choose the Find button. The Find dialog box displays the names of located files in the search results list. Right-clicking an item in the list loads the file into DesignCenter.

Browsing the Content of Files

Use the palette to browse the content of drawings and other sources. The palette displays preview images and descriptions that help you identify content. For example, if you select a drawing file in tree view, the palette displays icons for layers, blocks, xrefs, and so on. Selecting Blocks in tree view displays images for the drawing's block definitions in the palette, selecting Layers displays the drawing's layers, and so on.

Placing Content in Drawings

To place content in a drawing, you can drag items from the palette or the Find dialog box directly into an open drawing. You can also copy content to the Clipboard and paste it into a drawing.

To get started		
Action	**Menu**	**Toolbar**
Using DesignCenter	Tools ➤ AutoCAD ➤ DesignCenter	Standard

ONLINE HELP ADCENTER

Using External Information with AutoCAD LT

You can insert text files created in word processors into your drawings. You can also use the Windows object linking and embedding (OLE) feature with AutoCAD LT. Common uses of AutoCAD LT with external files include

- Inserting existing, preformatted text, or spreadsheets into drawing files
- Using bitmap images as clip art in AutoCAD LT drawings
- Adding an AutoCAD LT view to a word processor document

Using Imported Text in AutoCAD LT Files

You can save time by importing TXT or RTF files from other sources—for example, a text file of standard notes that you include in drawings. Instead of entering this information each time you use it, you can import the file. If you import text files using the Multiline Text Editor, the imported text retains its original formatting properties. The imported text becomes a text object that you can edit in AutoCAD LT.

You can also drag text files directly from Windows Explorer or use Windows editing commands to paste text from the Clipboard into your drawing file. In this case, inserted text uses the formats and fonts defined by the current AutoCAD LT text style.

Linking and Embedding Overview

When you use OLE to create compound documents, you decide whether you want to *embed* or *link* the inserted object.

- *Embedding* does not maintain a reference to the original file in the container file; if the original file is changed, the copy does not change.
- *Linking* ensures that changes to the original file are reflected in the container file.

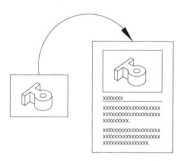

Linking and Embedding AutoCAD LT Information in Other Applications

Use the Clipboard to insert objects from AutoCAD LT into files created with other applications. Using the AutoCAD LT Cut and Copy commands and then pasting from the Clipboard into the container file creates embedded information. Using the Copy Link command before pasting with the container application's procedures for inserting linked data creates a linked object.

Linking and Embedding Objects in AutoCAD LT Files

You use the Insert Object dialog box to link an entire file to an AutoCAD LT drawing. You may want to include a bitmap image, a Microsoft® PowerPoint® presentation, or even a multimedia icon that is activated by double-clicking.

You embed an object in an AutoCAD LT drawing by pasting the Clipboard contents. Dragging items into AutoCAD LT from another active application window is the same as cutting and pasting. For example, you can embed a company logo created with another application by dragging the graphic or copying and pasting it into your drawing.

NOTE See your Windows documentation for more information about OLE and the use of standard Windows editing procedures for linking and embedding.

To get started		
Action	**Menu**	**Toolbar**
Importing text files into drawings	Draw ➤ Text ➤ Multiline Text	Draw
Linking objects from AutoCAD LT in other files	Edit ➤ Copy Link	
Linking objects in AutoCAD LT drawings	Insert ➤ Ole Object	

ONLINE HELP MTEXT, COPYLINK, COPYCLIP, CUTCLIP, INSERTOBJ, PASTESPEC, PASTECLIP

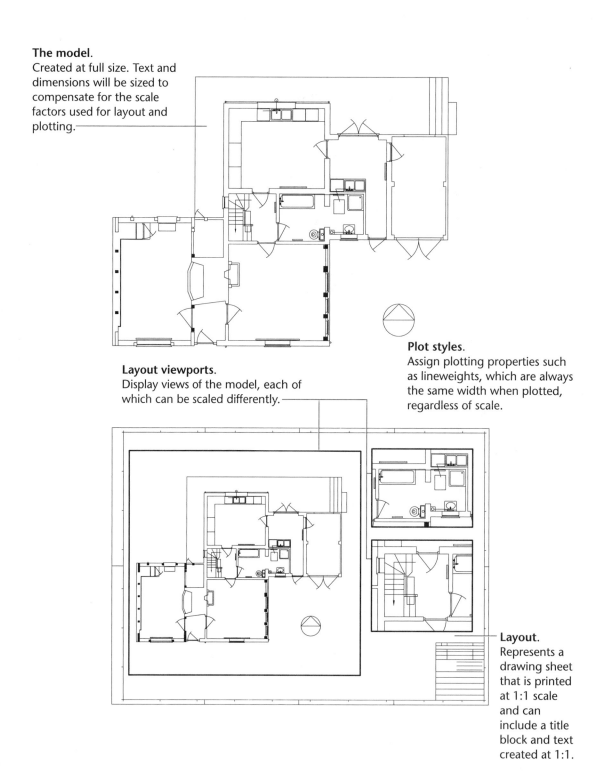

The model.
Created at full size. Text and dimensions will be sized to compensate for the scale factors used for layout and plotting.

Layout viewports.
Display views of the model, each of which can be scaled differently.

Plot styles.
Assign plotting properties such as lineweights, which are always the same width when plotted, regardless of scale.

Layout.
Represents a drawing sheet that is printed at 1:1 scale and can include a title block and text created at 1:1.

Creating Layouts and Plotting

14

The last part of the drawing process is producing output, whether you plot your drawings on paper or create files for use with other applications. This chapter explains the relationship between layouts and plotting, controlling how objects plot, setting up a plotter, and plotting your first drawing.

Printing and Plotting Overview

Understanding terms and concepts that relate to plotting makes your first plotting experience in AutoCAD LT®easier.

Plotter Manager

The Plotter Manager is a window that includes plotter configuration (PC3) files for every nonsystem printer that you install. Plotter configuration files can also be created for Windows®system printers if you want AutoCAD LT to use default properties different from those used by Windows. Plotter configuration settings specify port information, raster and vector graphics quality, paper sizes, and custom properties that depend on the plotter type.

The Plotter Manager contains the Add-a-Plotter wizard, which is the primary tool for creating plotter configurations. The Add-a-Plotter wizard prompts you for information about the plotter you want to set up.

Layouts

You can use a layout to show a preview of a plotted page. You can create as many layouts as you need for every drawing file. Each layout can be associated with a different page size and plotter.

Elements that only appear on a plotted page, such as title blocks and notes, are drawn in paper space in a layout. The objects in the drawing are created in model space on the Model tab. To view these objects in the layout, you create layout viewports.

Page Setups

When you create a layout, you specify a plotter, a page size, and a plot orientation. You can control these settings for layouts using the Page Setup dialog box. You can save page setups for use with other layouts. You can also save multiple page setups for each layout.

If you don't specify all the settings in the Page Setup dialog box when you create a layout, you can set up the page just before you plot. Or you can override a page setup when you plot. You can use the new page setup temporarily for the current plot, or you can save the new page setup.

Plot Styles

A plot style controls how an object or layer is plotted by determining plotted properties such as lineweight, color, and fill style. Plot style tables collect groups of plot styles. The Plot Style Table Manager is a window that shows all the plot style tables available in AutoCAD LT.

There are two plot style behavior options: color-dependent and named. A drawing can only use one type of plot style table. You can convert plot style tables from one type to the other. You can also change the plot style table behavior of a drawing once it has been set.

For *color-dependent plot style tables,* an object's color determines how it is plotted. The files have CTB extensions. You cannot assign color-dependent plot styles directly to objects. Instead, to control how an object is plotted, you change its color. For example, all red objects in a drawing plot the same way.

Named plot style tables use plot styles that are assigned directly to objects and layers. The files have STB extensions. Using them enables each object in a drawing to be plotted differently, independent of its color.

To get started		
Action	**Menu**	**Toolbar**
Creating a new layout	Insert ➤ Layout	Layouts
Starting the Plotter Manager	File ➤ Plotter Manager	
Creating a layout viewport	View ➤ Viewports	
Setting up the page	File ➤ Page Setup	

ONLINE HELP LAYOUT, PAGESETUP, PLOT, CONVERTPSTYLES, CONVERTCTB

Road Map to Creating Layouts and Plotting

The way you approach plotting differs depending on whether you start from a layout or from the Model tab. The information below assumes you are using the default settings for AutoCAD LT.

Plotting from a Layout

Plotting from a layout is the recommended approach.

To plot from a layout			
Action	**Dialog box/window**	**Required steps**	**Optional steps**
1. Set up plotter.	Plotter Manager		Add a plotter.
	Plotter Configuration Editor		Edit a plotter configuration.
2. Choose or create a layout.	N/A	Choose a layout tab.	Create a layout (use Create Layout wizard).
3. Choose or create a page setup.	Page Setup		Select a saved page setup.
	Page Setup *Plot Device tab*	Select a plotter.	Edit plotter properties. Select a plot style table. Edit a plot style table.
	Page Setup *Layout Settings tab*	Select page size and drawing orientation.	
4. Create viewports and determine scaling.	Viewports		Create layout viewports.
	N/A		Scale views in viewports (use Viewports toolbar, the ZOOM command, or the Properties window).
5. Plot.	Plot *Plot Device tab and Layout Settings tab*		Override page setup.
	Plot	Create hard copy.	Preview hard copy.

NOTE If you select a saved page setup, you can go directly to creating viewports. Also, you can use the Create Layout wizard to select a printer, paper size and orientation, and a title block, and then define and scale viewports.

Plotting from the Model Tab

For simple, single-view drawings, you can choose to plot from the Model tab.

To plot from the Model tab			
Action	**Dialog box**	**Required steps**	**Optional steps**
1. Set up plotter.	Plotter Manager		Add a plotter.
	Plotter Configuration Editor		Edit a plotter configuration.
2. Determine scaling.	N/A	Scale text, dimensions, linetypes, and title block, if any, so they will plot at correct size after model is scaled for plotting.	
3. Plot.	Plot *Plot Device tab*	Select a plotter.	Edit plotter properties. Select a plot style table. Edit a plot style table.
	Plot *Plot Settings tab*	Select page size and drawing orientation.	
	Plot *Plot Settings tab*	Select a plot area.	
	Plot *Plot Settings tab*	Select or set a plot scale.	
	Plot	Create hard copy.	Preview hard copy.

Working with Layouts

A paper space layout represents a drawing sheet. Layouts provide an easy method of setting up your page for plotting and previewing the final plot. Layouts show the page border and actual printing area. The page size and actual printing area are based on the printer or plotter assigned to the layout.

By default, a new drawing begins with two layouts in addition to the Model tab. You can create as many layouts as you need in a drawing. Each layout can be associated with a different output device or a different page setup.

You can move between the Model tab and layouts by clicking the Layout tabs at the bottom of the drawing area.

Creating Viewports in a Layout

When you create a new layout, you can choose to add one or more layout viewports. One layout viewport is added automatically. You use layout viewports to arrange views of your drawing on a Layout tab. By creating a layout viewport, you can view and edit objects residing on the Model tab. Each viewport can have its own scale, plot properties, and layer visibility settings.

For information about creating and working with viewports, see page 130.

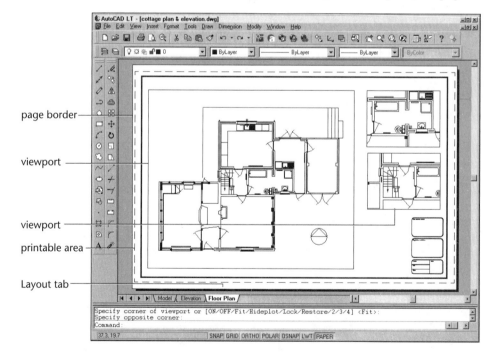

page border

viewport

viewport

printable area

Layout tab

Creating and Editing Layouts

You can create a layout using the Create Layout Wizard, insert a layout from an existing drawing template, or create a new layout from scratch. Once you create a layout, you can insert a title block and create or delete layout viewports. When creating a layout, you need to provide information about the page setup and plotter, including

- A printer or plotter to associate with the layout
- A paper size for the layout (based on the selected printer or plotter)
- The orientation of the paper

You can change any of this information or select additional page setup settings later.

Layouts can be edited at any point in the drawing process, even temporarily at plot time. You can rename, delete, and copy layouts easily by right-clicking the Layout tab.

To get started		
Action	**Menu**	**Toolbar**
Creating a new layout	Insert ➤ Layout	Layouts

ONLINE HELP LAYOUT, LAYOUTWIZARD, PAGESETUP, PLOT, MVIEW

Sizing and Scaling

Whether you plot from the Model tab or from a layout, all objects should be drawn at their actual size. When plotting from the Model tab, scale the title block around the objects and make the entire drawing smaller or larger to fit on the page at plot time. When plotting from a layout, insert the title block at actual size, create one or more layout viewports, and set a display scale for the objects from the model that are shown in each layout viewport. For more information on planning drawing units and scale, see page 98.

Scaling for Plotting from the Model Tab

After your objects are drawn, insert a title block and scale it up or down around the objects. Once the title block has been inserted, add dimensions and notes and adjust the global linetype scale.

Inserting the Title Block on the Model Tab

Invert the drawing's final plot scale to determine the scale factor when you insert the title block. For example, for a drawing with a plot scale of 1:2, scale up the title block by a factor of 2. For a scale of 1/4" =1'-0", use a factor of 48.

Because the title block is scaled up or down around the objects, scale it and all the objects in the drawing at plot time to fit on the paper. Dimensions, text, and linetypes must also be made proportionally larger or smaller to invert the effects of the plot scaling.

Scaling Text, Dimensions, and Linetypes on the Model Tab

The title block's scale factor is used to scale other objects. For example, you need to change the size of all the dimensions, while leaving the actual values unchanged. Change the value of the overall scale on the Fit tab of the Modify Dimension Style dialog box to the scale that you used to insert the title block.

Use this same value as a scale factor for the text in your drawing. For example, to create 1/4" text in a drawing with a scale of 1/4" =1'-0", you use a scale factor of 48. In this example, the text needs to be 12" high to plot at 1/4".

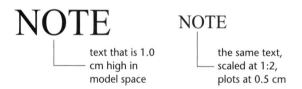

NOTE
text that is 1.0
cm high in
model space

NOTE
the same text,
scaled at 1:2,
plots at 0.5 cm

Use this same value for the linetype scale so that all the dashed and noncontinuous linetypes in your drawing are plotted at the appropriate size.

Scaling for Plotting from a Layout

Scaling on a Layout tab is simpler than on the Model tab. The title block, text, and linetypes created directly on the layout all remain actual size when plotted, because the layout shows the actual paper size and is plotted at 1:1.

Scaling Text, Dimensions, and Linetypes in Layout Viewports

To specify scale factors for text created in model space and displayed in layout viewports, you invert the viewport's scale. For example, if viewport scale is 1/4" = 1'0", you multiply the text size that you want by 48. Dimensions created in model space and displayed in layout viewports are scaled automatically when Scale Dimensions to Layout is selected on the Fit tab of the Dimension Style Manager. By default, the scale factor for linetypes displayed in layout viewports adjusts automatically to the viewport scale.

To get started		
Action	**Menu**	**Toolbar**
Changing dimension styles	Dimension ➤ Style	Dimension
Changing layout/viewport display scale	View ➤ Zoom ➤ Scale	Standard/Viewports

ONLINE HELP INSERT, DIMSTYLE, STYLE, LTSCALE, PSLTSCALE, LWEIGHT, CELTSCALE

Choosing and Configuring Plotters

You must choose a printer or plotter when plotting and when setting up a layout. If your output device is not listed in the Plot or Page Setup dialog boxes, or if its settings are incorrect, you can easily add or edit printer and plotter configurations.

AutoCAD LT supports a wide range of printers and plotters. Devices with a Windows printer driver installed are available automatically when you plot from AutoCAD LT unless the plotting option to hide system printers has been selected. Many plotters that do not have Windows drivers, or nonsystem plotters, can be configured for use with AutoCAD LT using drivers provided either by Autodesk or by the plotter manufacturer.

You can also use plotter drivers to save your drawings in a variety of file formats. If you need to create DWF (drawing Web format) files to view drawings in a Web browser, PostScript files for use with page layout programs, or raster files, you can configure an appropriate plotter driver in the Plotter Manager.

Adding a Plotter

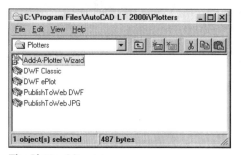

The Plotter Manager

The Plotter Manager is a folder in the *AutoCAD LT 2000i* folder that provides a method for adding, deleting, and changing plotter configurations. Plotter configuration files have a *.pc3* extension and are stored in the *Plotters* folder.

To add a plotter configuration, double-click the Add-a-Plotter wizard in the Plotter Manager. The Add-a-Plotter wizard will prompt you for information about your plotter, including

- Whether the plotter is attached to your computer or on a network
- The type of plotter, including manufacturer and model
- Whether to use a plotter configuration file from previous versions of AutoCAD LT
- Whether to output to a computer port or file, and which port to use
- A unique name for the new plotter configuration

Once you enter this information, a new PC3 file is created, and this plotter is available when you are setting up a layout and plotting.

Changing a Plotter Configuration

The Plotter Configuration Editor makes changes to plotter configurations. To start the Plotter Configuration Editor, either double-click the PC3 file or choose Properties in the Plot dialog box. Use it to

- Edit the port or file output information
- Change or add paper sizes and layouts
- Control vector and raster graphic output
- Calibrate your plotter
- Set any of your plotter's custom properties

If you make changes to a plotter configuration while plotting, you can choose to affect only the current plot or to change the PC3 file.

For more information about installing a printer or plotter, see appendix A, page 265. For information about installing a specific device, see online Help.

To get started	
Action	**Menu**
Starting the Plotter Manager	File ➤ Plotter Manager

ONLINE HELP PLOTTERMANAGER, OPTIONS

Controlling Plot Styles

You can precisely control the way that objects are plotted by using plot styles and plot style tables. A plot style is an object property, like color, that can be assigned to layers or to individual objects in drawings. A plot style table is a grouping of plot styles. Plot style tables can be assigned to layouts.

Color-Dependent and Named Plot Style Tables

By default, AutoCAD LT employs *color-dependent plot style tables*. When you use color-dependent plot style tables, the way an object is plotted is directly related to its color. For example, every red object in a drawing plots the same way. Color-dependent plot style tables are used to control the lineweight of plotted objects.

You can also use *named plot style tables*. In a named plot style table, the way an object is plotted is determined by the plot style assigned to it, independent of its color. Named plot style tables control an object's color and lineweight separately. You can assign plot styles to objects using the Properties window. For information on setting object properties, see page 136.

A color-dependent plot style table can be thought of as a special named plot style table in which there are 256 plot styles, one for every color. You cannot add or delete plot styles from a color-dependent plot style table.

You choose whether to use color-dependent or named plot style tables for new drawings in the Options dialog box.

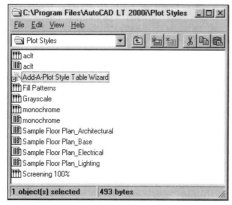

The Plot Style Manager

Adding a Plot Style Table

You can add, delete, and change plot style tables in the Plot Style Manager. Like the Plotter Manager, this is a folder. It contains all of your plot style tables. Color-based plot style tables have a *.ctb* extension. Named plot style tables have an *.stb* extension. You can easily add either type of plot style table by double-clicking the Add-a-Plot Style Table wizard. You can import pen settings from previous versions of AutoCAD LT when you add a plot style table. All of the plot style tables of one type listed in the Plot Style Manager are available in the Plot and Page Setup dialog boxes.

Choosing a Plot Style Table

You can select an appropriate plot style table when setting up a layout or whenever you plot. AutoCAD LT includes several standard plot style tables of both types:

- *Aclt*. Standard plot style table
- *Fill Patterns*. Different object fill patterns for the first nine colors
- *Grayscale*. All colors plotted with their nearest grayscale equivalent
- *Monochrome*. All colors plotted as black
- *Screening 50%*. All colors plotted at half intensity

You can also choose not to use any plot style table by selecting None when plotting or when setting up the page.

To get started	
Action	**Menu**
Starting the Plot Style Manager	File ➤ Plot Style Manager

ONLINE HELP STYLESMANAGER, PLOTSTYLE, PLOT

Plotting from the Model Tab and from a Layout

The process for plotting is similar whether from the Model tab or from a layout. Once the drawing has been scaled and sized appropriately, the plotting process can be broken into three parts:

- What to plot
- How to plot
- Where to plot

To determine what to plot, you control the visibility and Plot/Don't Plot property layers. You also select the area of the drawing that you want to plot.

To determine how objects plot, you control the scale, color, lineweight, and linetype settings. With some plotters, you control some of these features at the plotter. Whether or not these features are controlled at the plotter, they can be controlled with plot style tables. Some plotters offer a choice between hardware and software control of virtual pens. If hardware control is selected, plot style settings, except for virtual pen number, are ignored.

To determine where the plot is produced, you choose an output device. Select which printer or plotter you want to use, and then select a page size and orientation.

Using the Plot Dialog Box

In the Plot dialog box, you control your plot setup using the Plot Device tab and the Plot Settings tab.

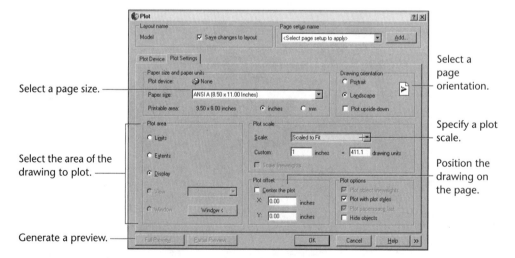

Select a page size.

Select the area of the drawing to plot.

Generate a preview.

Select a page orientation.

Specify a plot scale.

Position the drawing on the page.

On the Plot Device tab, you select the printer or plotter and the plot style table you want to use. You can also select whether you want to stamp the plotted drawing with identifying information such as drawing name, layout name, login name, plotting device name, paper size, date and time, and plot scale. On the Plot Settings tab, you set the area of the drawing to plot, the scale of the plot, the size of the page, the orientation of the drawing on the page, and the position of the drawing on the page.

NOTE It is a good practice to generate a full plot preview. If the image is not correct, make changes to the page setup and the plot style table attached to the layout.

To get started		
Action	Menu	Toolbar
Opening the Plot dialog box	File ➤ Plot	Standard

ONLINE HELP PLOT, PLOTSTAMP

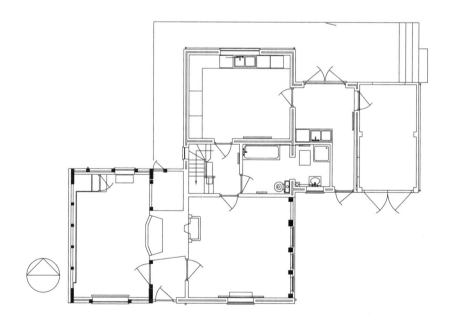

The drawing you will plot in this tutorial

The Layout and Plotting Tutorial

15

This tutorial provides an introduction to editing and then plotting a drawing, from both the Model tab and a Layout tab. The step-by-step procedures provide an overview of the steps that you must take to prepare a drawing for plotting.

AutoCAD LT® provides two methods for plotting drawings. The exercises in this tutorial demonstrate both approaches.

For detailed information about some of the commands you will use, see online Help or the appropriate sections in this guide.

In this chapter

- Plotting from the Model Tab
- Setting Up a Layout
- Plotting from a Layout

Plotting from the Model Tab

In these exercises, you will learn how to set up an existing drawing to be plotted from the Model tab and from a Layout tab. If you are comfortable with plotting from model space, you can skip to page 259.

You begin by opening a drawing, and then you prepare it for plotting by inserting a title block and adjusting the dimensions.

To open an existing drawing

1 From the File menu, choose Open.
2 Navigate to the *AutoCAD LT 2000i\Help* folder and select *tutorial1.dwg*.
3 Choose Open.

This is a drawing of an elevation and a floor plan. It contains several layers to organize the objects in the drawing.

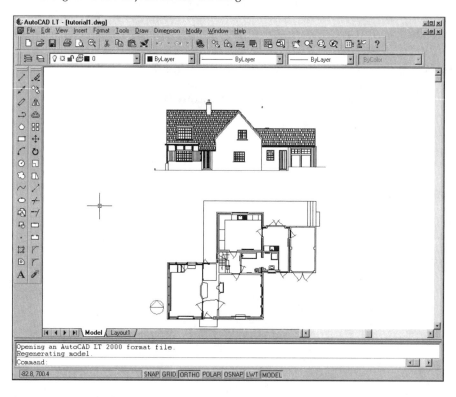

In this exercise, you will insert a title block, adjust the scaling of dimensions, and plot the drawing. When plotting from the Model tab, you scale the title block to fit around the objects in the drawing. Because the drawing is scaled at plot time, the text and dimensions must be sized and scaled accordingly.

Inserting a Title Block

All the objects in this drawing were created at actual size. You will need to scale the title block around the objects any time you are not plotting at 1:1. The value that is used to scale the title block will also be used to change the size of the dimensions and text.

To insert a title block

1 Make sure that you are on the Model tab by clicking the Model tab at the bottom of the graphics area.

2 From the Insert menu, choose Block.

3 In the Insert dialog box, select Letter (portrait) from the drop-down list.

4 Under Insertion Point, make sure the Specify On-screen check box is cleared. Then enter **0.0** for the X, Y and Z values to place the title block in the lower-left corner of your drawing.

5 Under Scale, clear the Specify On-screen check box. Then enter **128** for the X, Y, and Z values.

This determines the size of the title block and also indicates that the scale of the drawing is 1/128, or 3/32"=1'-0", when plotted (because $128 \times 3/32" = 12"$ or $1'-0"$).

6 Under Rotation, clear the Specify On-screen check box. Then enter **0** for the Angle to keep the title block horizontal.

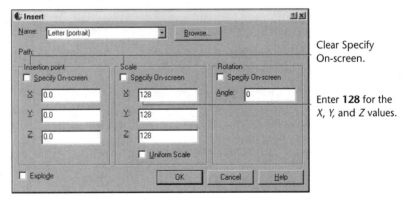

Clear Specify On-screen.

Enter **128** for the X, Y, and Z values.

7 Choose OK.

8 From the View menu, choose Zoom ➤ Extents.

The objects in the drawing are actual size, and the title block has been scaled up 128 times. In order for the title block to fit on a piece of paper at the correct size, it needs to be scaled down at plot time. All the objects in the drawing, including the dimensions and text, are also scaled.

Adjusting the Scaling of Dimensions

This drawing already contains several dimensions on a frozen layer. Their features are too small based on the scale of the title block. For example, the dimension text is 0.125 inches. To produce text that is 0.125 plotted inches, the text needs to be 0.125 x 128 = 16. You correct the size of the dimension text and all dimension features by changing the dimension scale factor.

To adjust scaling of dimensions

1 From the Format menu, choose Layer.

2 In the Layer Properties Manager, select the Model Space Dimensions layer. Click the Freeze/Thaw icon (the snowflake) to thaw the layer, and then choose OK.

3 From the Dimension menu, choose Style.

4 In the Dimension Style Manager, choose Modify.

5 Choose the Fit tab.

A typical dimension contains lines, arrows, and text. The Fit tab controls the placement of these components.

6 Under Scale for Dimension Features, enter **128** in the Use Overall Scale Of box.

The value used for the overall scale is the same as the scale factor used for the title block.

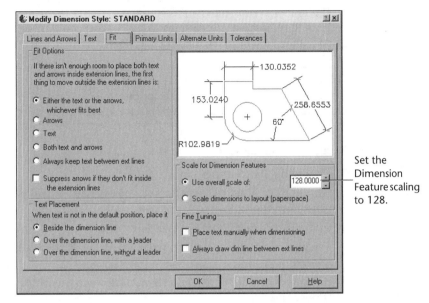

The dialog box contains:

Modify Dimension Style: STANDARD

Tabs: Lines and Arrows | Text | Fit | Primary Units | Alternate Units | Tolerances

Fit Options

If there isn't enough room to place both text and arrows inside extension lines, the first thing to move outside the extension lines is:

◉ Either the text or the arrows, whichever fits best
○ Arrows
○ Text
○ Both text and arrows
○ Always keep text between ext lines

☐ Suppress arrows if they don't fit inside the extension lines

Text Placement

When text is not in the default position, place it

◉ Beside the dimension line
○ Over the dimension line, with a leader
○ Over the dimension line, without a leader

Drawing dimensions shown: 130.0352, 153.0240, 258.6553, 60°, R102.9819

Scale for Dimension Features

◉ Use overall scale of: 128.0000
○ Scale dimensions to layout (paperspace)

Fine Tuning

☐ Place text manually when dimensioning
☐ Always draw dim line between ext lines

OK | Cancel | Help

Set the Dimension Feature scaling to 128.

7   Choose OK. Then choose Close to exit each dialog box. Note that the text and tick marks in the dimensions now appear to be the correct size for this drawing.

Setting Up the Plot

In this exercise, you follow a three-step process to plot from the Model tab. First, you will select the plotting device. Second, you will select the area of the drawing to plot. Finally, you specify how the drawing will be placed on the paper.

To choose a plot device and plot style table

1   From the File menu, choose Plot to display the Plot dialog box.

2   Choose the Plot Device tab, where you select a plotter and a plot style table.

3   Under Plotter Configuration, select a plotter from the drop-down list.

This list displays all the plotters that are installed in Windows® as well as any for which you have installed drivers separately. If you have not configured a printer or plotter, select the *DWF ePlot.pc3* device.

4 Under Plot Style Table (Pen Assignments), select the *monochrome.ctb* file from the Name list. When AutoCAD LT asks if you want to apply this plot style table to all the layouts, choose No.

NOTE This drawing uses color-dependent plot style tables. Thus, the plot style tables in the drop-down list are all color-dependent. The *monochrome.ctb* file plots every color in the drawing with black ink, even on a color printer.

To specify an area to plot

1 Choose the Plot Settings tab.

On this tab you set the area to plot, the orientation and position of the paper, and the scale.

2 Under Plot Area, choose the Window button.

The graphics area is temporarily displayed so that you can define a window.

3 Hold down the SHIFT key and right-click. From the Object Snap menu, choose Endpoint.

4 Use the scroll bar if necessary and select one corner of the title block.

5 Hold down the SHIFT key and right-click. From the Object Snap menu, choose Endpoint.

6 Use the scroll bar if necessary and select the opposite corner of the title block.

To set the scale and preview the plotted drawing

1 Under Plot Scale, in the Scale box, select 3/32"=1'-0".

The proportion of plotted inches (Custom) to drawing units is 1:128.

2 Under Drawing Orientation, select Portrait.

3 Preview the plot by choosing the Full Preview button at the bottom of the Plot Dialog box. Press ESC to close the preview.

4 Depending on the plotter you selected, the plot may appear to be off-center because of the space needed to feed the paper through your plotter. If you know the values used by your plotter, enter the values under Plot Offset. If you don't know the values, select Center the Plot.

5 Choose OK to plot the drawing.

6 From the File menu, choose Save As. In the Save Drawing As dialog box, enter **Tutorial1 Complete** in the File Name box and then choose Save.

7 From the File menu, choose Close.

Setting Up a Layout .

In this exercise, you will learn how to edit the page setup for an existing layout, how to adjust the viewport configuration for a layout, how to set the viewport scale, and how to set up dimensions in a layout.

You begin by opening a drawing.

To open an existing drawing

1 From the File menu, choose Open.

2 Navigate to the *AutoCAD LT 2000i\Help* folder and select *tutorial2.dwg*.

3 Choose Open.

This is a drawing of a floor plan and elevation. It contains several layers to organize the objects in the drawing.

To edit an existing layout

1 Choose the Elevation Layout tab below the graphics area.

The Elevation layout uses a page setup that includes the plot area and page size. A specific plotter configuration is also associated with the Elevation layout.

2 From the File menu, choose Page Setup.

3 On the Plot Device tab, under Plot Style Table (Pen Assignments), select the *monochrome.ctb* file. If prompted, choose not to apply the plot style table to all other layouts.

4 Select Display Plot Styles, and then choose OK.

The drawing is no longer displayed in color. It is now black and white because the layout shows a preview of the drawing as it will be plotted.

5 Choose the Model tab. Note that the model is still displayed in color.

To create a new layout

1 From the Insert menu, choose Layout ➤ Layout Wizard.

The Layout Wizard guides you through the creation of a layout.

2 Begin by entering a name for the new layout. Call this layout **Elevation and Floor Plan**. Choose Next.

3 Select the printer that you want to use to plot this layout from the list. If you do not have a printer to use, select *DWF ePlot.pc3*. Choose Next.

4 The paper sizes available in the Paper Size window are based on the printer that you selected. Select Letter or ANSI A (8.5 × 11.0 inches) for the paper size. Make sure that the Paper Size in Units lists a width of 11.0 inches (279.4 mm) and a height of 8.5 inches (215.9 mm). Choose Next.

If your printer does not support this paper size, select a comparable size. This may affect the placement of the drawing on the sheet when you plot.

5 Select Portrait as the orientation. Choose Next.

6 Select None from the list of available title blocks. Choose Next.

You will insert a title block once the layout is created.

7 Under Viewport Setup, select Array. Then set 2 rows and 1 column. Set the spacing between rows to 0.25 inches (6.35 mm). This creates two viewports, vertically aligned, with a gap between them. Leave the Viewport Scale as Scaled to Fit. You will change the scale later. Choose Next.

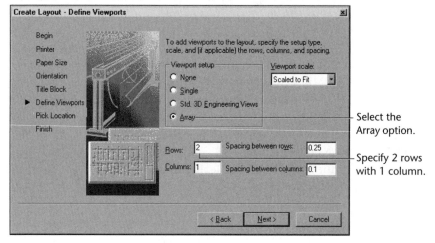

8 Choose Select Location. In the graphics area, click and drag to create a rectangle that is just inside the printable area (the dashed lines).

9 Choose Finish to complete the creation of the new layout and viewports.

To insert a title block into a layout

1 Make sure that you are on the Elevation and Floor Plan tab.

2 From the Insert menu, choose Block.

3 In the Insert dialog box, select Letter (portrait) from the drop-down list.

4 Under Insertion Point, make sure the Specify On-screen check box is cleared. Then enter **0.0** for the *X*, *Y*, and *Z* values to place the title block in the lower-left corner of the printable area of the layout. The location may require some adjustment.

5 Under Scale, make sure the Specify On-screen check box is cleared. Then enter **1** for the *X*, *Y*, and *Z* values, because the layout is plotted full scale.

6 Under Rotation, make sure the Specify On-screen check box is cleared. Then enter **0** for the Angle to keep the title block horizontal.

7 Choose OK.

8 If the title block that you inserted is not within the lower-left corner of the printable area, from the Modify menu, choose Move. Select the title block by clicking it. Then press ENTER. Click in the drawing, drag until the lower-left corner of the title block is just inside the lower-left corner of the dotted rectangle, and click again.

Setting Up the Viewports

Now that the layout viewports have been created, you need to specify the scale of the model space view displayed in each viewport. When you change the scale of a viewport, you change the zoom magnification. To change the portion of the model space drawing seen in the viewport without changing the scale, use the PAN command.

To set up the viewports to plot

1 Select both of the viewports by clicking their borders.

2 From the Modify menu, choose Properties. In the Properties window, choose the Alphabetic tab. Click the Layer box and select the Viewport layer. Press ESC twice to remove selection from the viewports and clear their grips.

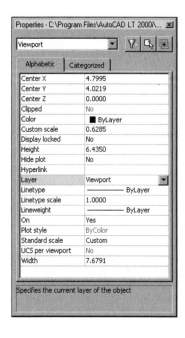

3　Select the top viewport by clicking its border.

This viewport will display the elevation.

4　In the Properties window, choose the Alphabetic tab. Click the Standard Scale box and select 3/32"=1' from the list of scales.

The model space objects are scaled correctly for plotting at 3/32"=1'.

5　Double-click inside the top viewport to switch to model space. From the View menu, choose Pan ➤ Real Time. Drag the image in the viewport until only the elevation is displayed. Press the ESC key to exit the PAN command.

6　Click inside the bottom viewport to make it active.

You will set the scale of this viewport using the ZOOM command.

7　From the View menu, choose Zoom ➤ Center. Click near the middle of the floor plan.

8　On the command line, enter **1/128XP**. The *XP* indicates that the magnification factor is relative to the paper space layout.

9　If necessary, pan to adjust the location of the objects in the viewport.

10　From the Format menu, choose Layer. In the Layer Properties Manager, select the Viewport layer. Click the Plottable/Non-Plottable icon to turn off plotting for the Viewport layer. Choose OK.

Plotting is turned off for the viewport borders, but the objects in the viewport are still plotted.

To create dimensions in a layout

1　On the status bar, click Model to switch to paper space.

2　From the Tools menu, choose Drafting Settings. On the Object Snap tab, make sure Object Snap On and Endpoint are selected. Choose OK.

3 From the Dimension menu, choose Style.

4 In the Dimension Style dialog box, choose Modify. On the Primary Units tab under Measurement Scale, set the Scale Factor to 128. Select Apply to Layout Dimensions Only. Choose OK. Then choose Close.

You entered 128 to compensate for the fact that objects shown in the bottom viewport are 1/128th actual size. In the next step, you add a dimension to the bottom viewport. At 1/128th actual size, the dimension text would be too small to be legible. Setting the scale to 128 increases the dimension text to the appropriate size. This is the same reason that you entered 128 for the scale of the title block in the previous exercise.

5 From the Dimension menu, choose Linear. Create a horizontal dimension for the length of the building using objects in the bottom viewport.

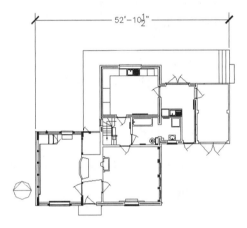

Plotting from a Layout

Now that you have created a layout and have prepared the dimensions and viewports for plotting, you are ready to plot the drawing.

To plot a drawing from a layout

1 From the File menu, choose Plot.

2 Choose the Plot Device tab.

Note that the plotter you chose in the wizard is still selected.

3 Under Plot Style Table (Pen Assignments), select the *monochrome.ctb* file for the plot style table.

4 On the Plot Settings tab, under Plot Area, select Extents.

5 Under Drawing Orientation, select Portrait.

6 Under Plot Offset, select Center the Plot.

7 Under Plot Scale, set the scale of the plot to 1:1.

Because you are plotting from a layout, the title block is actual size and the drawing is scaled by the viewport.

8 Choose Full Preview at the bottom of the dialog box. If the preview looks correct, press ESC and choose OK.

9 From the File menu, choose Save As. In the Save Drawing As dialog box, enter **Tutorial2 Complete** in the File Name box and then choose Save.

For more information about printing and plotting, see page 238. Regarding layouts, see page 242. Regarding plot style tables, see page 248. Regarding sizing and scaling, see page 244. Regarding blocks, see page 186.

Configuring Plotters and Printers

AutoCAD LT® supports many plotters and printers for producing hard-copy output of your drawings. You can output to files in a variety of formats. This chapter provides basic printer and plotter configuration information. Configuration information specific to a supported device, such as hardware connections, switch settings, cabling diagrams, and software settings, can be found in online Help.

In this appendix

- Using Drivers for Plotter Support
- Using the Plotter Manager
- Using the HDI System Printer Driver
- Using an HDI Nonsystem Driver
- Setting the Time-Out Value for Devices
- Configuring File Format Drivers

Using Drivers for Plotter Support

AutoCAD LT 2000i uses the HDI (Heidi® Device Interface) to communicate with output devices. These drivers fall into three categories: HDI system printer drivers, HDI nonsystem drivers, and file format drivers. In addition, Hewlett-Packard has provided an optimized Microsoft® Windows® system printer driver for DesignJet plotters.

HDI System Printer Driver

The system printer driver, *gdiplot7.hdi*, acts as a gateway to any previously installed Windows system printers. The printers or plotters can be locally connected or networked. The *gdiplot7.hdi* file sends raster information to a raster-capable Windows system printer.

Although all installed Windows system printers are automatically available within AutoCAD LT, you can use the Add-a-Plotter wizard to configure a system printer's default values differently for AutoCAD LT and Windows.

NOTE You can turn off the display of Windows system printers on the Plotting tab of the Options dialog box.

HDI Nonsystem Drivers

Nonsystem drivers plot directly to many types of printers and plotters. The printers or plotters can be locally connected or networked.

File Format Drivers

File format drivers send data to files and do not print on paper. AutoCAD LT uses file format drivers to produce DWF (drawing Web format) files, PostScript files, and raster files in several formats. This approach to creating DWF files is also called ePlot.

Hewlett-Packard DesignJet System Printer Driver

DesignJet customers should use the system printer driver provided with AutoCAD LT. It has been optimized for use with AutoCAD LT. Use the Windows Add Printer Wizard in the Control Panel to install this system driver. Do not use the AutoCAD LT Add-a-Plotter wizard.

Using the Plotter Manager

If you want to plot using one of the nonsystem plotter drivers, save files in a different format, or configure a Windows system printer with different settings for AutoCAD LT, use the Autodesk Plotter Manager.

AutoCAD LT stores information about the media and plotting device in plotter configuration (PC3) files. Plot configurations are portable and can be shared in an office or on a project. If you calibrate a plotter, the calibration information is stored in a plot model parameter (PMP) file that you can attach to any PC3 files you create for the calibrated plotter.

If you always use system printers and only change the paper size, you might not need to use the Plotter Manager. However, PC3 files for Windows system drivers are often specific to the platform you are using. Therefore, you might need to save different PC3 files for use with different operating systems, for example, Windows 98 and Windows NT.

You can configure AutoCAD LT for many devices, and you can store multiple configurations for a single device. Each plotter configuration contains information such as the device driver and model, the output port to which the device is connected, and various device-specific settings. After you create a PC3 file, it is available in the list of plotter configuration names on the Plot Device tab in the Plot and Page Setup dialog boxes.

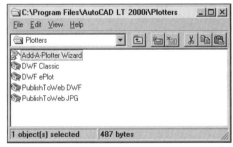

The Plotter Manager: a folder in the AutoCAD LT 2000i folder

To create these PC3 files, use the Add-a-Plotter wizard in the Plotter Manager. The Plotter Manager is a Windows Explorer window. The Add-a-Plotter wizard is modeled after the Windows Add Printer wizard. You can create any number of plotter device configurations that use either the Windows system printer drivers or Autodesk nonsystem plotter drivers. By default, your configurations are stored in the *AutoCAD LT 2000i\Plotters* folder.

Opening the Plotter Manager

You can use any of the following methods to open the Plotter Manager:

- From the File menu, choose Plotter Manager.
- Double-click the Autodesk Plotter Manager icon in the Windows Control Panel.
- On the command line, enter **plottermanager**.
- From the Tools menu, choose Options. On the Plotting tab, choose Add or Configure Plotters.

Editing Your Plotter Configuration Files

After you create a plotter configuration (PC3) file using the Add-a-Plotter wizard, you can edit the file using the Plotter Configuration Editor. The Plotter Configuration Editor provides options for modifying a plotter's port connections and output settings, including media, graphics, physical pen configuration, custom properties, initialization strings, calibration, and user-defined paper sizes. You can drag these options from one PC3 file to another.

There are several ways to start the Plotter Configuration Editor:

- From the File menu, choose Page Setup ➤ Properties.
- Double-click a PC3 file in Windows Explorer. (By default, PC3 files are stored in the *AutoCAD LT 2000i\Plotters* folder.)

The Plotter Configuration Editor contains three tabs to set general information, port settings, and plot options dependent on the type of plotter.

NOTE When you edit a system driver, most of the settings in the Plotter Configuration Editor are not available. You change most system driver settings in the Custom Properties dialog box.

Using the HDI System Printer Driver

With the HDI Windows system printer driver, you can use any plotter or printer you have configured with Windows. Any printing device supported by Windows can be used with the Windows system driver. It is recommended that you use the Windows system printer driver for raster output devices.

NOTE The system printer driver supports raster output. However, the ability of the device connected as the system printer to output raster and vector data sent by AutoCAD LT may be limited.

Configuring the HDI System Driver

There are several ways to modify the default settings for a Windows system printer without creating a PC3 file. For example, you can modify the properties systemwide in the Control Panel. You can also choose Properties in the Plot dialog box and plot without saving the properties.

Setting up the Windows system printer for AutoCAD LT consists of two steps:

1 Configure the system printer in Windows. (See the Microsoft documentation for your operating system and the documentation provided by your printer manufacturer.)

2 If you want to use default values that differ from those used by Windows, configure the Windows system printer as the AutoCAD LT plotter. Save this configuration in a PC3 file.

Creating a PC3 File for a Windows System Printer

Use the Add-a-Plotter wizard to add a system printer.

The list of printers available as system printers includes all printers known to the operating system. Do not select My Computer or Network Plotter Server; these are nonsystem choices. If you want to connect to a printer that is not in the list, you must first add the printer using the Windows Add Printer wizard in the Control Panel.

NOTE If your printer or plotter supports both PCL and PostScript, there may be more than one system driver available. PCL is sometimes a better choice for CAD plotting because it supports merge control for most devices. PCL sometimes prints raster images that cause memory overflow when printing with PostScript.

A PC3 file for the newly configured plotter appears in the *Plotters* folder, and the plotter is available for plotting in the list of devices.

Using an HDI Nonsystem Driver

For pen plotters, it is recommended that you use the nonsystem driver appropriate to your device rather than the Windows system printer driver. After you add the plotter, a PC3 file for the newly configured plotter appears in the *Plotters* folder and the plotter is available for plotting in the list of devices.

When you configure a nonsystem driver, you specify the kind of port to which the device is connected and you can browse to select local serial and parallel ports or a network printer. If the hard-copy device has only one type of port, you are offered only the appropriate choice.

To configure a PostScript device, select Adobe from the Manufacturers list.

If your plotter is not listed, and you have an HDI nonsystem driver disk for your plotter, choose Have Disk to locate the HIF driver file, and then install the driver supplied with your plotter.

You can change the default settings for the plotter by choosing Edit Plotter Configuration on the Add Plotter - Finish page. You can also perform a plot calibration test on your newly configured plotter by choosing Calibrate Plotter on the Add Plotter - Finish page.

NOTE You cannot use ADI (Autodesk Device Interface) drivers with AutoCAD LT 2000i.

Configuring a Network Nonsystem Plotter

If you choose a network printer connected to a computer that is running a different version of Windows, you might see a one-time prompt to install the Windows system driver for the remote device on your system.

You can use an HDI driver configured for your specific plotter to plot to a device across a network. You use a Windows system printer driver to make the device browsable.

To view and select a remote network plotter, you must install a Windows system printer driver for that plotter on the remote system. If the device is connected to the remote system using a serial port, use the Windows Control Panel to set the serial port parameters to match the device's communication parameters and cabling. You must set the serial port's baud rate, data bits, parity, stop bits, and handshaking before the device can be used. Verify that you can plot or print to the device by using the Windows system printer driver.

When you specify a server, it must already exist on the network. For more information, see your system administrator.

You must use the universal naming convention (UNC). The correct format of a UNC path is *server name**share name*. You can select an existing share name on your network by choosing Browse.

Resolving Windows Print Manager Conflicts

If you configure an HDI hard-copy driver and a Windows system printer for the same locally connected plotter, the HDI driver cannot connect directly to the local port because the Windows system printer driver has control over it. The driver output is rerouted to the Windows print spooler. You will see an alert if this happens. You can use a setting on the Plotting tab in the Options dialog box turn off the alert.

If the plotter is connected to a serial port, the Windows Control Panel settings for that port should match the settings of the plotter and should be appropriate for the cabling you have used. You can verify that these settings are correct by printing to the conflicting Windows system printer.

Plotting from an HDI driver through the spooler is similar to plotting to a file because there is only one-way communication with the plotter. Performance varies depending on the device.

Setting the Time-Out Value for Devices

The time-out value determines how long the plotter can instruct AutoCAD LT to stop sending data while it empties its buffer. After the plotter empties its buffer, it accepts more data from AutoCAD LT. When you choose a time-out value, specify how much time should elapse before AutoCAD LT prompts you to abort the plot. If your drawings are complex, or contain OLE objects, or if your pen speed is very slow, set the time-out value higher than the default (30 seconds). If you begin to receive numerous time-out prompts, your time-out setting is probably too low. You can set the time-out value during the initial configuration or during configuration at plot time.

To set the time-out value for a local, nonsystem plotter

1 From the File menu, choose Plotter Manager.

2 In the Plotter Manager, double-click the plotter configuration you want to edit.

3 In the Plotter Configuration Editor, choose the Ports tab. Then select the port that you want to use.

4 Choose Configure Port.

  ■ To configure a parallel port, in the Transmission Retry box, enter the time-out value in milliseconds.

  ■ To configure a serial port, in the Timeout and Output Timeout box, enter the time-out values in milliseconds.

To set the time-out value for network or system printers In Windows NT 4.0

You must have appropriate user rights to modify the printer's settings. See your system administrator.

1 From the Windows Start menu, choose Settings ➤ Printers.

2 Right-click the printer you want, and then choose Properties.

3 In the Properties dialog box, choose the Ports tab.

4 On the Ports tab, select the LPT port that the printer uses, and then choose Configure Port.

5 In the Transmission Retry box, enter the number of seconds.

To set the time-out value for network or system printers in Windows 95 and Windows 98

1 From the Windows Start menu, choose Settings ➤ Printers.

2 Right-click the printer you want, and then choose Properties.

3 In the Properties dialog box, choose Details.

4 In the Timeout area, enter the number of seconds.

Configuring File Format Drivers

AutoCAD LT can use the file format drivers to output files in a variety of formats, including DWF (drawing Web format), PostScript, HP-GL and HP-GL/2, and the following raster file formats:

- CALS MIL-R-28002A Type 1 (CCITT G4 2D Compression)
- Independent JPEG Group JFIF (JPEG Compression)
- MS-Windows BMP (Uncompressed DIB)
- Portable Network Graphics PNG (LZH Compression)
- TIFF Version 6 (CCITT G4 2D Compression)
- TIFF Version 6 (Uncompressed)
- TrueVision TGA Version 2 (Uncompressed)
- ZSoft PC Paintbrush PCX (ZSOFT PACKBITS Compression)

Each file format has its own options and variants.

The driver behaves as a plotter and creates a file. The file format drivers are available when configuring a nonsystem printer. See online Help for more information.

ONLINE HELP Plotter, PLOTTERMANAGER

Configuring a Digitizing Tablet

B

This appendix provides the information you need to configure a digitizing tablet using the Wintab driver. Each section has information that helps you configure your digitizing tablet to work with AutoCAD LT®. A basic tablet configuration with default selections is provided.

AutoCAD LT can be set up to accept input from both a digitizing tablet and your mouse, or a tablet can be used in place of a mouse as a system pointer to make full use of the graphical interface.

In this appendix

- Configuring the Wintab Driver
- Using a Mouse Versus a Digitizing Tablet
- Restricting Mouse Input
- Configuring Fixed and Floating Screen-Pointing Areas
- Working in Tablet Mode
- Reinitializing the Tablet

Configuring the Wintab Driver

AutoCAD LT supports Wintab-compatible digitizing tablets. The digitizing puck or stylus can be used in place of a mouse as a system pointer, and it can also be used as an absolute pointing device to trace drawings into AutoCAD LT (by turning Tablet mode on).

Wintab is a Windows specification that is used to make the digitizing tablet capable of being both a system pointer and an absolute pointing device. The ADI Wintab driver developed by Autodesk is installed with AutoCAD LT. It provides an interface so a Wintab-compatible digitizing tablet can be used as a system pointer to choose menu items and drawing objects in AutoCAD LT.

To configure Windows 95, Windows 98, or Windows NT 4.0 for the Wintab driver provided with the digitizer, follow the installation procedure supplied with the digitizer. Wintab drivers are not distributed with AutoCAD LT. The digitizer must work with Windows to work with AutoCAD LT. You can use a digitizer with AutoCAD LT only by configuring Windows for use with the Wintab driver. Make sure that the Wintab driver is configured for the correct digitizer model and the correct number of buttons on the puck or stylus.

Windows NT must have both a Wintab System driver and an ADI Wintab driver compiled for 32-bit Windows.

With Windows 95 you can use either a 16- or a 32-bit Wintab driver but only with the 32-bit ADI Wintab driver. If you use a 16-bit Wintab driver with Windows 95, you must install a driver in order for the 32-bit ADI Wintab driver to call the 16-bit system resources of the 16-bit Wintab System driver.

The following table displays the modules required to run Wintab drivers. The translation program is provided by the Wintab driver manufacturer and should be on the diskette that accompanies the driver. For more information or to obtain the Wintab driver, contact the hardware manufacturer.

Required Wintab module drivers			
Platform	System driver	Translation program	ADI Wintab driver
Windows 95	16-bit	Required	32-bit
	32-bit	None	32-bit
Windows NT 4.0	32-bit	None	32-bit

Using a Mouse Versus a Digitizing Tablet

You can configure AutoCAD LT for a mouse, a digitizing tablet, or both. Before you configure the digitizing tablet, the entire tablet area is a fixed screen-pointing area. Inside a screen-pointing area, the tablet pointing device (puck or stylus) acts like a mouse.

Using Mouse Devices

A mouse is a relative screen-pointing device. Because it does not provide a one-to-one correspondence between the mouse position and the drawing, it cannot be used to trace existing paper drawings or to support tablet menus. A mouse usually returns coordinates relative to its last placement. This makes a mouse the best tool to use to access the Windows graphical user interface.

Although you can use Microsoft®Windows®and AutoCAD LT without a mouse, a mouse or other pointing device is recommended to take full advantage of the AutoCAD LT graphical interface.

To configure the mouse

1 From the Windows Start menu, choose Settings ➤ Control Panel.

2 In the Control Panel window, double-click the Mouse icon.

3 In the Mouse Properties dialog box, you can swap the functions of the left and right mouse buttons, change the mouse tracking speed, and alter the double-click speed of the mouse. By convention, the left mouse button is the pick button.

Using Digitizing Tablets

A digitizing tablet is an absolute pointing device: each point on the tablet has a one-to-one correspondence to a specific location in the drawing, making the tablet the most useful tool for digitizing drawings in AutoCAD LT. Tablets are typically configured in two ways, for a tablet overlay or for digitizing existing drawings or photographs.

The purpose of calibration is to establish a proportional relationship between the tablet surface and the actual size of the object being drawn. After a tablet is calibrated, it can be used to trace geometry from an existing drawing or photograph into an AutoCAD LT drawing, simultaneously creating accurate dimensions in the AutoCAD LT model. Points digitized from the drawing or photograph represent actual coordinates. In AutoCAD LT, using a tablet in this manner is called Tablet mode. You can turn Tablet mode on and off by using TABLET, choosing Tablet from the Tools menu, or pressing F4 on your keyboard.

When the tablet is configured, and Tablet mode is off, portions of the tablet surface are designated as menu areas and a screen-pointing area. A tablet configured with the AutoCAD LT tablet overlay provides convenient access to the most common AutoCAD LT drawing tools and can be customized to include your favorite features and macros. Cells A1 through I25 on the AutoCAD LT tablet overlay are intentionally left blank to accommodate user-defined shortcuts and macros.

Before you configure the tablet, attach the tablet overlay to the tablet so that it does not move during use, assuring that you track to the menu areas that you configure.

NOTE Although the tablet overlay is not required for tablet configuration, it is recommended that you use it.

Restricting Mouse Input

AutoCAD LT can accept input from both a mouse and a digitizer. Use the following procedure to designate input from both pointing devices.

To set up AutoCAD LT to use both a mouse and a digitizer

1 From the Tools menu, choose Options.

2 In the Options dialog box, choose the System tab.

3 On the System tab, select Wintab Compatible Digitizer. Then select Digitizer and Mouse.

If you are digitizing a drawing into AutoCAD LT, you may not want accidental movement of the mouse to move the crosshairs.

When AutoCAD LT first starts, the entire tablet is a fixed screen area. Inside a screen area, the tablet pointer acts like a mouse. If you select Digitizer Only input, you won't see the crosshairs moving. But, remember, the tablet pointer acts as a mouse inside a screen area.

To designate the tablet as the only input device for AutoCAD LT, use the following procedure.

To limit AutoCAD LT input to the digitizer

1 Calibrate the tablet as described in the procedure on page 285.

2 From the Tools menu, choose Options.

3 In the Options dialog box, choose the System tab.

4 On the System tab, under Wintab Digitizer, select Digitizer Only. Then choose OK.

NOTE You are now limited to using the tablet for input and only when Tablet mode is turned on. You cannot specify points in the drawing area with the mouse.

Configuring Fixed and Floating Screen-Pointing Areas

AutoCAD LT uses the concept of screen-pointing areas for tablets. A screen-pointing area is a rectangular region on the tablet surface within which the tablet pointer mimics system mouse movement. The screen areas map to the computer display *absolutely*. In other words, when the cursor is within a screen-pointing area, the tablet pointer can access windows, menus, and other applications outside the AutoCAD LT drawing area. You can configure a maximum of two screen-pointing areas for a tablet: one fixed and one floating.

After you configure AutoCAD LT, but before you configure your tablet, the entire surface of the tablet is actually the *fixed screen-pointing area*. At that point, the tablet pointer performs like a mouse. You can change the size of the fixed screen-pointing area by specifying a new size using the Cfg (Configuration) option of TABLET. It is recommended that you specify a small screen area on your tablet that maps to the entire screen on your monitor.

If you want to turn on Tablet mode and digitize points into AutoCAD LT, you cannot use a fixed screen-pointing area. When Tablet mode is on, there is a one-to-one correspondence between the digitizer and the drawing.

You can configure the *floating screen-pointing area* to expand the size of the pointing area on the tablet for creating and selecting objects. With a floating screen-pointing area, you can access toolbars and pull-down menus anywhere on the tablet surface and toggle them off when you have finished. When prompted, you can specify the size of the floating screen area and special toggling options. However, the floating screen-pointing area cannot be calibrated for tracing and does not support tablet menu access.

NOTE The floating screen-pointing area takes precedence over the fixed screen-pointing area, which in turn takes precedence over the tablet.

You can switch between the fixed and floating screen-pointing areas by using F12 or by using a toggle button that you designate during configuration. Some Wintab drivers allow access to button commands only if the cursor is outside the screen-pointing area. If you notice that the buttons on your tablet pointer are not responding appropriately, move the pointer anywhere outside the fixed screen-pointing area and then press the button again.

Configuring the Tablet for a Menu Overlay

To configure your tablet to use an overlay, it is recommended that you select the default tablet menus, columns, and rows that are provided. The following illustration shows the tablet overlay supplied by AutoCAD LT. After the tablet menus have been configured, the procedure prompts you for the fixed and floating screen-pointing areas, along with the option to use a tablet pointer button to toggle between the fixed and floating screen-pointing areas.

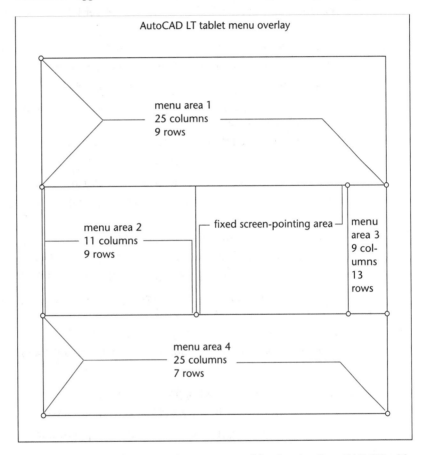

AutoCAD LT tablet menu overlay

menu area 1
25 columns
9 rows

menu area 2
11 columns
9 rows

fixed screen-pointing area

menu area 3
9 columns
13 rows

menu area 4
25 columns
7 rows

The following procedure configures your tablet for the AutoCAD LT tablet overlay. Defaults that are displayed may depend upon the specific digitizer you are configuring.

To configure the tablet for use with the tablet overlay

1 At the Command prompt, enter **tablet**, and then enter **cfg** at the following prompt.

   Option (ON/OFF/CAL/CFG):

2 At the following prompt, enter **4**.

   Enter number of tablet menus desired (0-4) <0>:

3 When prompted, digitize the upper-left, lower-left, and lower-right corners of menu area 1.

   In response to the following prompts, press ENTER.

   Enter the number of columns for menu area 1, 1 to 4991 <25>:

   Enter the number of rows for menu area 1, 1 to 1839 <9>:

4 When prompted, digitize the upper-left, lower-left, and lower-right corners of menu area 2.

   In response to the following prompts, press ENTER.

   Enter the number of columns for menu area 2, 1 to 2202 <11>:

   Enter the number of rows for menu area 2, 1 to 1809 <9>:

5 When prompted, digitize the upper-left, lower-left, and lower-right corners of menu area 3.

   In response to the following prompts, press ENTER.

   Enter the number of columns for menu area 3, 1 to 539 <9>:

   Enter the number of rows for menu area 3, 1 to 1806 <13>:

6 When prompted, digitize the upper-left, lower-left, and lower-right corners of menu area 4.

   In response to the following prompts, press ENTER.

   Enter the number of columns for menu area 4, 1 to 5004 <25>:

   Enter the number of rows for menu area 4, 1 to 1407 <7>:

7 In response to the following prompt, enter **y**.

   Do you want to respecify the Fixed Screen Pointing Area? <N>:

   When prompted, digitize the lower-left and upper-right corners of the fixed screen-pointing area.

8 Respond to the following prompts to designate your floating screen-pointing area.

   In response to the following prompt, enter **y**.

   Do you want to specify the Floating Screen Pointing Area? <N>:

In response to the following prompt, enter **y** or **n**.

Do you want the Floating Screen Pointing Area to be the same size as the Fixed Screen Pointing Area? <Y>:

If you entered **n**, digitize the lower-left and upper-right corners of the floating screen-pointing area.

9 In response to the following prompt, enter **n** or press any button other than the pick button on the tablet pointer to designate it as the on/off button for the floating screen-pointing area.

The F12 key will toggle the Floating Screen Pointing Area ON and OFF. Would you like to specify a button to toggle the Floating Screen Area? <N>:

Working in Tablet Mode

If you want to digitize drawings, photographs, or other graphic material, you must first calibrate the tablet. If you want to digitize points in AutoCAD LT with Tablet mode turned on, you may want to configure the template for zero menus with a screen-pointing area of any reasonable size. The fixed screen-pointing area can be bigger or smaller than the default screen-pointing area on the AutoCAD LT template (tablet menu).

Using Tablet Menus in Tablet Mode

You can also calibrate the tablet to digitize drawings and keep the tablet menu areas configured; however, make sure that the configured area does not overlap the area you are tracing. Depending on the size of your digitizer and the size of the paper drawing, you may have to turn off your tablet menu area until you have finished digitizing your paper drawing.

Calibrating Your Tablet

If you want to switch from a tablet calibrated for tracing drawings to a tablet configured for a tablet overlay with a different sized screen-pointing area, the tablet must be reconfigured.

To configure or reconfigure the tablet for digitizing drawings

1 Turn on your digitizer.

2 At the Command prompt, enter **tablet**, and then enter **cfg** at the next prompt.

3 At the following prompt, enter **0**.

Enter number of tablet menus desired (0-4) <0>:

4 At the following prompt, enter **y**.

Do you want to respecify the Fixed Screen Pointing Area? <N>

5 At the following prompts, digitize an area that is greater than or equal to the area you want to use to digitize drawings.

Digitize lower left corner of Fixed Screen Pointing Area:
Digitize upper right corner of Fixed Screen Pointing Area:

6 At the following prompt, enter **y** if you want a floating screen-pointing area.

Do you want to specify the Floating Screen Pointing Area? <N>

7 If you entered **y** in step 6, at the following prompt, enter **y** or **n**.

Do you want the Floating Screen Pointing Area to be the same size as the Fixed Screen Pointing Area? <Y>:

If you entered **n**, digitize a floating screen-pointing area of the size you want. If you need to, you can repeat this step to resize the area.

8 In response to the following prompt, enter **y** or **n**.

The F12 key will toggle the Floating Screen Pointing Area ON and OFF. Would you like to specify a button to toggle the Floating Screen Area? <N>:

9 If you entered **y** at the prompt in step 8, at the following prompt, press any button other than the pick button.

Press any nonpick button that will become the toggle for the Floating Screen Area:

Calibration maps the points on the tablet to the points on the paper drawing you want to trace. When you use the Cal option of TABLET, you specify points on the tablet with the tablet pointer and then give those points coordinate values. You can specify a minimum of two points that define a rectangular area.

Calibration requires specifying a minimum of two points, but specifying five points is recommended. Choose points that are not close to one another and for which you can enter precise X,Y coordinate values.

When calibrating the tablet, it is recommended that you enter lower-left coordinates before upper-right coordinates. If you calibrate only two points and the second point is below and to the right of the first point (with positive coordinates), AutoCAD LT point mapping becomes unreliable.

To calibrate the tablet

1 Tape the paper drawing at the top of the active tablet surface area.

2 At the Command prompt, enter **tablet**. Then enter **cal**.

3 Using the first button on the tablet pointer, click a point on the tablet for which you know the X,Y coordinate.

NOTE When clicking points, it is recommended you hold the puck stylus in both hands and, looking down from the top, align the puck crosshairs as accurately as possible with the specified location in the drawing. An error or inaccuracy when clicking the calibration points represents a residual error throughout your work.

AutoCAD LT prompts you for the X,Y coordinate values.

4 Enter the *X,Y* coordinate value for the point you specified.

5 Repeat steps 3 and 4.

6 Press ENTER to end the command, or repeat steps 3 and 4 to calibrate more points.

After calibrating the tablet, set the transformation type to Orthogonal, Affine, or Projective.

- *Orthogonal* specifies translation, uniform scaling, and rotation with two calibration points. Use Orthogonal for dimensionally accurate paper drawings and paper drawings in which the portion to be digitized is long and narrow, with most points confined to single lines.
- *Affine* specifies arbitrary linear transformation in two dimensions consisting of translation, independent *X*- and *Y*-scaling, rotation, and skewing with three calibration points. Use Affine when horizontal dimensions in a paper drawing are stretched with respect to vertical dimensions and lines that are supposed to be parallel actually are parallel.
- *Projective* specifies a transformation equivalent to a perspective projection of one plane in space onto another plane with four calibration points. A projective transformation provides a limited form of what cartographers call rubber sheeting, in which different portions of the tablet surface are stretched by varying amounts. Straight lines map into straight lines. Parallel lines do not necessarily stay parallel. Projective transformation corrects parallel lines that appear to converge.

If only two points are entered, AutoCAD LT automatically computes an orthogonal transformation. If it is successful, AutoCAD LT ends the command.

If three or more points are entered, AutoCAD LT computes the transformation in each of the three types to determine which best fits the calibration points. If more than four points are entered, computing the best-fitting projective transformation can take a long time. You can cancel the process by pressing ESC.

When the computations are complete, AutoCAD LT displays a table with the number of calibration points and a column for each transformation type. The following information is provided under each column: outcome of fit, RMS error, standard deviation, point of largest residual, and point of second-largest residual.

If there have been no failures of projection transformation, AutoCAD LT prompts:

Select transformation type . . .
Orthogonal / Affine / Projective? <Repeat table>: Enter an option or press ENTER

Only transformation types for which the outcome was Success, Exact, or Canceled are included in this prompt. A projective transformation can be specified even if it was canceled; AutoCAD LT uses the result computed at the time you canceled.

After you have calibrated the tablet, the coordinates showing on your screen should be coincident with the coordinates in the paper drawing. You can now trace a drawing with the tablet and the tablet pointer. Enter an AutoCAD LT drawing command, and use the pointer to specify points on the material you are tracing. The points you specify become digitized to create a drawing.

Using Editing Commands in Tablet Mode

Any command that requires you to select objects with the tablet pointer still works in Tablet mode. For example, to erase an object, start the ERASE command and move the tablet pointer until the pickbox is over the object.

Testing Tablet Calibration

If your drawing is not correct after you calibrate your tablet, double-check the accuracy of your tablet. To test the scaling accuracy of your tablet, use the Cal option of TABLET.

To test the tablet calibration

1 At the Command prompt, enter **tablet**. Then enter **cal**.

2 Specify a point in the lower-left corner of the tablet.

   Write down the coordinate values AutoCAD LT displays on the status bar. These values represent the tablet's raw coordinate values before they are processed by AutoCAD LT.

3 In response to the prompt for point 1, enter the values shown in the coordinate display, and mark that point on the tablet.

4 Specify a point in the lower-right corner of the tablet.

   Move the cursor to the right of the first point, keeping the current *Y* value as close to the *Y* value of the first point as possible. Write down the current coordinate values AutoCAD LT displays on the status bar.

5 In response to the prompt for point 2, enter the current values shown in the coordinate display, and mark that point on the tablet.

Move the cursor so that the *X* value is the same as the *X* value of the first point, and the *Y* value is the same as the *Y* value of the second point.

6 Enter the *X* and *Y* values of the coordinate and mark those points on the tablet.

7 Press ENTER to calculate the transformation.

The calculations should show an RMS (root-mean-square) error very close to 0. RMS measures how close AutoCAD LT has come to finding a perfect fit. The goal is to find the smallest RMS error. The affine transformation should be exact.

Tablets vary in accuracy. Accuracy specifications are listed in the manual provided with each tablet model. AutoCAD LT can compensate for a paper-to-drawing scaling inaccuracy by using the three-point affine transformation during tablet calibration. If the inaccuracy in the orthogonal transformation is greater than the inaccuracy of manually positioning the tablet's cursor, use the affine transformation.

Reinitializing the Tablet

For AutoCAD LT to run properly, all the input and output ports, the *aclt.pgp* file, and peripheral devices attached to your computer—pointing device, video display, and plotter—must be properly initialized. If your tablet hardware settings change and need to be reinitialized for any reason, use REINIT to reinitialize the tablet parameters with AutoCAD LT.

To reinitialize the tablet

1 At the Command prompt, enter **reinit**.
2 In the Reinitialization dialog box, under I/O Port Initialization, select Digitizer.
3 Under Device and File Initialization, select Digitizer.

NOTE Some Wintab drivers require a computer shutdown and startup sequence in order to reinitialize properly. If reinitializing the tablet does not correct your problem, shut down your computer and restart it. Then verify that the Wintab driver is functional in Windows before running AutoCAD LT.

ONLINE HELP TABLET

Task-Based Command Summary

This appendix gives a task-based overview of the AutoCAD LT® commands and how to access them. The information for each command includes name, toolbar button (defaults only), menu options (defaults only), alias (abbreviation you can enter instead of the entire name), and description.

An apostrophe at the beginning of the command name indicates that it is a transparent command; that is, it can be used while another command is running if the apostrophe is typed in.

If you need more information about any of these commands, see online Help..

In this appendix

- Understanding the Workspace
- Opening, Closing, and Saving Drawings
- Drawing Setup
- Precision Drawing
- Changing Views
- Drawing Objects
- Making Modifications
- Using Blocks, or Symbols, and Hatches Repeatedly
- Adding Text
- Dimensioning
- Information Sharing
- Creating Layouts and Plotting
- Configuring a Digitizing Tablet
- Managing and Repairing Drawing Files
- Working with Scripts

Command	Button	Menu option	Alias	Description
Understanding the Workspace				
ABOUT		Help/ About AutoCAD LT		Displays information about AutoCAD LT
ASSIST		Help/ Active Assistance		Opens the Active Assistance window, which provides automatic or on-demand context-sensitive information
'BLIPMODE			BM	Controls the display of marker blips
CUSTOMIZE		Tools/Customize/ Toolbars	TO	Displays, hides, and customizes toolbars
DBLCLCKEDIT				Controls double-click behavior
'GRAPHSCR				Switches from the text window to the graphics area
'HELP		Help/AutoCAD LT Help		Displays online Help
MENULOAD		Tools/ Customize/Menus		Loads partial menu file
MENUUNLOAD		Tools/ Customize/Menus		Unloads partial menu file
MULTIPLE				Repeats the next command until canceled
OPTIONS		Tools/Options	OP	Customizes the AutoCAD LT settings
'REDRAW		View/Redraw	R	Refreshes the display of the current viewport
REGEN		View/Regen	RE	Regenerates the drawing and refreshes the current viewport
REGENALL		View/Regen All	REA	Regenerates the drawing and refreshes all viewports

Command	Button	Menu option	Alias	Description
'SETVAR			SET	Lists or changes the values of system variables
SYSWINDOWS				Arranges MDI Windows and icons in AutoCAD LT
'TEXTSCR		View/Display/ Text Window		Opens the AutoCAD LT text window
TOOLBAR		View/Toolbars		Displays, hides, and customizes toolbars

Opening, Closing, and Saving Drawings

Command	Button	Menu option	Alias	Description
CLOSE		File/Close		Closes the current drawing
CLOSEALL				Closes all currently open drawings
ENDTODAY				Closes the Today window
NEW		File/New	N	Creates a new drawing file
OPEN		File/Open		Opens an existing drawing file
QSAVE		File/Save		Quickly saves the current drawing
QUIT		File/Exit		Exits AutoCAD LT
SAVE			SA	Saves the current drawing
SAVEAS		File/Save As		Saves an unnamed drawing with a file name or renames the current drawing
TODAY		Tools/Today *or* File/New		Opens the Today window

Command	Button	Menu option	Alias	Description
Drawing Setup				
'COLOR		Format/Color	COL	Sets the color for new objects
'LAYER		Format/Layer	LA	Manages layers and layer properties
LAYOUT		Insert/Layout/ New Layout		Creates and modifies drawing Layout tabs
LIMITS		Format/ Drawing Limits	LM	Sets and controls the limits of the grid display in the current Model or Layout tab
LINETYPE		Format/Linetype	LTYPE	Loads and sets linetypes
'LTSCALE		Format/Linetypes/ Detail	LTS	Sets the global linetype scale factor
LWEIGHT		Format/Lineweight	LW	Sets the current lineweight, lineweight display options, and lineweight units
MODEL				Switches from a Layout tab to the Model tab and makes it current
OPTIONS		Tools/Options	OP	Customizes the AutoCAD LT settings
'UNITS		Format/Units	UN	Controls coordinate and angle display formats and determines precision
Precision Drawing				
'APERTURE				Controls the size of the object snap target box
DSETTINGS		Tools/Drafting Settings	DS, SE	Sets grid and snap, polar tracking, and object snap modes
'ELEV				Sets elevation and extrusion thickness of new objects
'GRID				Displays a dot grid

Command	Button	Menu option	Alias	Description
HIDE		View/Hide	HI	Regenerates a 3D model with hidden lines suppressed
'ISOPLANE			IS	Specifies the current isometric plane
LIMITS		Format/ Drawing Limits	LM	Sets and controls the limits of the grid display in the current Model or Layout tab
'ORTHO			OR	Constrains cursor movement
'OSNAP		Tools/Drafting Settings	OS	Sets running object snap modes
'SNAP			SN	Restricts cursor movement to specified intervals
TRACKING (with LINE)		Object snap menu		Locates a point from a series of temporary points
UCS		Tools/New UCS	UC	Manages user coordinate systems
UCSICON		View/Display/ UCS Icon		Controls the visibility and placement of the UCS icon
UCSMAN		Tools/Named UCS	UC	Manages defined user coordinate systems

Changing Views

Command	Button	Menu option	Alias	Description
DDVPOINT			VP	Sets the three-dimensional viewing direction
DSVIEWER		View/ Aerial View		Opens the Aerial View window
DVIEW			DV	Defines parallel projection or perspective views
MSPACE			MS	Switches from paper space to a model space viewport
MVIEW		View/Viewports/ 1, 2, 3, 4, Viewports	MV	Creates and controls layout viewports

Command	Button	Menu option	Alias	Description
'PAN		View/ Pan/Realtime	P	Moves the view in the current viewport
PLAN		View/3D Views/ Plan View		Displays the plan view of a user coordinate system
PSPACE			PS	Switches from a model space viewport to paper space
VIEW		View/Named Views	V	Saves and restores named views
VIEWRES				Sets the resolution for objects in the current viewport
VPOINT		View/3D Views/ VPOINT	VP	Sets the viewing direction for a 3D visualization of the drawing
VPORTS		View/ Viewports		Divides the graphics area into multiple viewports
'ZOOM		View/Zoom	Z	Increases or decreases the apparent size of objects in the current viewport

Drawing Objects

Command	Button	Menu option	Alias	Description
3DPOLY		Draw/3D Polyline		Creates a polyline of line segments in 3D space
ARC		Draw/Arc	A	Creates an arc
BOUNDARY		Draw/Boundary		Creates a polyline or a region from an enclosed area
CIRCLE		Draw/Circle	C	Creates a circle
'COLOR		Format/Color	COL	Sets the color for new objects
CONVERT				Converts legacy 2D polylines and hatches to an optimized format
'DDPTYPE		Format/ Point Style		Specifies the display mode and size of point objects

Command	Button	Menu option	Alias	Description
DLINE		Draw/ Double Line	DL	Creates a double line using straight line segments and arcs
DONUT		Draw/Donut	DO	Creates filled circles and rings
DRAWORDER		Tools/Display Order	DR	Changes the display order of images and other objects
ELLIPSE		Draw/Ellipse	EL	Creates an ellipse or an elliptical arc
INTERSECT		Modify/Region/ Intersect	IN	Combines selected regions by intersection
LINE		Draw/Line	L	Creates straight line segments
LINETYPE		Format/Linetype	LTYPE	Loads and sets linetypes
LWEIGHT		Format/Lineweight	LW	Sets the current lineweight, lineweight display options, and lineweight units
PLINE		Draw/Polyline	PL	Creates 2D polylines
POINT		Draw/Point	PT, PO	Creates a point object
POLYGON		Draw/Polygon	POL	Creates an equilateral closed polyline
PROPERTIES		Tools/Properties	PROPS	Controls properties of existing objects
PROPERTIESCLOSE			PRCLOSE	Closes the Properties window
RAY		Draw/Ray		Creates a semi-infinite line
RECTANG		Draw/Rectangle	REC	Draws a rectangular polyline
REGION		Draw/Region	REG	Converts an object that encloses an area into a region object
SHADE			SH	Displays a flat-shaded image of the drawing in the current viewport

Command	Button	Menu option	Alias	Description
SHADEMODE				Shades the objects in the current viewport
SOLID			SO	Creates solid-filled triangles and quadrilaterals
SPLINE		Draw/Spline	SPL	Creates a nonuniform rational B-spline (NURBS) curve
SUBTRACT		Modify/Region/ Subtract	SU	Combines selected regions by subtraction
UNION		Modify/Region/ Union	UNI	Combines selected regions by addition
XLINE		Draw/ Construction Line	XL	Creates an infinite line

Making Modifications
Selecting Objects

FILTER				Creates filters for object selection
GROUP		Tools/ Group Manager	G	Manages saved sets of objects called groups
QKUNGROUP		Tools/Ungroup		Removes a group definition from a drawing
QSELECT		Tools/Quick Select		Creates a selection set based on filtering criteria
SELECT				Places selected objects in the previous selection set

Making Modifications
Changing Shapes

BREAK		Modify/Break	BR	Breaks the selected object between two points

Command	Button	Menu option	Alias	Description
CHAMFER		Modify/Chamfer	CHA	Bevels the edges of objects
DIVIDE		Draw/Point/Divide	DIV	Places evenly spaced point objects or blocks along the length or perimeter of an object
EXPLODE		Modify/Explode	X	Breaks a compound object into its component objects
EXTEND		Modify/Extend	EX	Extends an object to meet another object
FILL				Controls the filling of solids and wide polylines
FILLET		Modify/Fillet	F	Rounds and fillets the edges of objects
LENGTHEN		Modify/Lengthen	LEN	Changes the length of objects and the included angle of arcs
MEASURE		Draw/Point/ Measure	ME	Places point objects or blocks at measured intervals on an object
PEDIT		Modify/Object/ Polyline	PE	Edits polylines
REVCLOUD		Tools/Revcloud	RC	Creates a polyline of sequential arcs to form a cloud shape
SCALE		Modify/Scale	SC	Enlarges or reduces objects equally in the *X*, *Y*, and *Z* directions
SPLINEDIT		Modify/Object/ Spline	SPE	Edits a spline or spline-fit polyline
STRETCH		Modify/Stretch	S	Moves or stretches objects
TRIM		Modify/Trim	TR	Trims objects at a cutting edge defined by other objects

Command	Button	Menu option	Alias	Description
Making Modifications				
Copying, Moving, and Erasing Objects				
ARRAY		Modify/Array	AR	Creates multiple copies of objects in a pattern
COPY			CP	Duplicates objects
COPYBASE		Edit/Copy with Base Point		Duplicates objects along with a specified base point
COPYCLIP		Edit/Copy		Copies objects to the Clipboard
CUTCLIP		Edit/Cut		Copies objects to the Clipboard and erases the objects from the drawing
ERASE		Modify/Erase	E	Removes objects from a drawing
MIRROR		Modify/Mirror	MI	Creates a mirror image copy of objects
MOVE		Modify/Move	M	Displaces objects a specified distance in a specified direction
MREDO			MR	Reverses the effects of several previous UNDO or U commands
OFFSET		Modify/Offset	O, OF	Creates concentric circles, parallel lines, and parallel curves
OOPS			OO	Restores erased objects
PASTECLIP		Edit/Paste	PC	Inserts data from the Clipboard
PASTEORIG		Edit/Paste to Original Coordinates		Pastes a copied object into a new drawing using the coordinates from the original drawing
PASTESPEC		Edit/Paste Special	PA	Inserts data from the Clipboard and controls the format of the data

Command	Button	Menu option	Alias	Description
REDO		Edit/Redo		Reverses the effects of one previous UNDO or U command
RMLIN		Insert/Markup		Inserts markups from an RML file into a drawing
ROTATE	↻	Modify/Rotate	RO	Rotates objects about a base point
U				Reverses the most recent action
UNDO	↶			Reverses the effect of commands

Making Modifications
  Changing Properties

Command	Button	Menu option	Alias	Description
CHANGE			-CH	Changes the properties of existing objects
CHPROP				Changes the color, layer, linetype, linetype scale factor, lineweight, plotstyle, and thickness of an object
MATCHPROP		Modify/ Match Properties	MA	Applies the properties of a selected object to other objects
PROPERTIES		Tools/Properties	PROPS	Controls properties of existing objects
PROPERTIESCLOSE			PRCLOSE	Closes the Properties window

Making Modifications
  Making Inquiries

Command	Button	Menu option	Alias	Description
AREA		Tools/Inquiry/Area	AA	Calculates the area and perimeter of objects or of defined areas
'DIST		Tools/Inquiry/ Distance	DI	Measures the distance and angle between two points
'ID		Tools/Inquiry/ ID Point		Displays the coordinate values of a location

Command	Button	Menu option	Alias	Description
LIST		Tools/Inquiry/List	LS	Displays database information for selected objects
MASSPROP		Tools/Inquiry/Mass Properties		Calculates and displays the mass properties of regions
PURGE		File/Drawing Utilities/Purge	PR, PU	Removes unused objects such as blocks or layers from the drawing
RENAME		Format/Rename	REN	Changes the names of named objects such as blocks and layers

Using Blocks, or Symbols, and Hatches Repeatedly

Command	Button	Menu option	Alias	Description
ADCENTER		Tools/AutoCAD DesignCenter	ADC, CE	Manages and inserts content such as blocks, xrefs, and hatch patterns
ATTDEF		Draw/Block/Define Attributes	AT	Creates an attribute definition
'ATTDISP		View/Display/Attribute Display	AD	Globally controls attribute visibility
ATTEDIT		Modify/Attribute/Single	AE	Edits the variable attributes of a block
ATTEXT		Tools/Attribute Extraction	AX	Extracts attribute data
'BASE		Draw/Block/Base	BA	Sets the insertion base point for the current drawing
BHATCH		Draw/Hatch	H	Fills an enclosed area with an associative hatch pattern
BLOCK		Draw/Block/Make	B	Creates a block definition from objects you select
BLOCKICON				Generates preview images for blocks displayed in AutoCAD DesignCenter
EXPLODE		Modify/Explode	X	Breaks a compound object into its component objects

Command	Button	Menu option	Alias	Description
GETENV				Shows values of specified registry variables
HATCH			-H	Fills an area with a nonassociative hatch pattern
HATCHEDIT		Modify/Object/Hatch	HE	Modifies an existing hatch object
INSERT		Insert/Block	I	Inserts a block or another drawing
PASTEBLOCK		Edit/Paste as Block		Pastes a copied block into a new drawing
REVDATE		Tools/Time and Date Stamp	RD	Inserts or updates a block containing user name, current time and date, and drawing name
SETENV				Sets values of specified registry variables
WBLOCK			W	Writes objects or a block to a new drawing file

Adding Text

Command	Button	Menu option	Alias	Description
DDEDIT		Modify/Object/Text	ED	Edits text, dimension text, and attribute definitions
FIND		Edit/Find		Finds, replaces, selects, or zooms to specified text
MTEXT		Draw/Text	T, MT	Creates a multiple-line text object
'QTEXT			QT	Controls the display and plotting of text and attribute objects
'SPELL		Tools/Spelling	SP	Checks spelling of selected text
'STYLE		Format/Text Style	ST	Creates, modifies, or sets named text styles

Command	Button	Menu option	Alias	Description
TEXT			TX	Displays text on screen as it is entered

Dimensioning

Command	Button	Menu option	Alias	Description
DDEDIT		Modify/Object/Text	ED	Edits text, dimension text, and attribute definitions
DIMALIGNED		Dimension/ Aligned	DAL	Creates an aligned linear dimension
DIMANGULAR		Dimension/ Angular	DAN	Creates an angular dimension
DIMBASELINE		Dimension/ Baseline	DBA	Continues a linear, angular, or ordinate dimension from the baseline of the previous or a selected dimension
DIMCENTER		Dimension/ Center Mark	DCE	Creates the center mark or the centerlines of circles and arcs
DIMCONTINUE		Dimension/ Continue	DCO	Continues a linear, angular, or ordinate dimension from the second extension line of the previous or a selected dimension
DIMDIAMETER		Dimension/ Diameter	DDI	Creates diameter dimensions for circles and arcs
DIMEDIT			DED	Edits dimensions
DIMLINEAR		Dimension/Linear	DLI	Creates linear dimensions
DIMORDINATE		Dimension/Ordinate	DOR	Creates ordinate point dimensions
DIMOVERRIDE		Dimension/Override	DOV	Overrides dimension system variables
DIMRADIUS		Dimension/Radius	DRA	Creates radial dimensions for circles and arcs

Command	Button	Menu option	Alias	Description
DIMSTYLE		Format/ Dimension Style	D	Creates and modifies dimension styles
DIMTEDIT		Dimension/ Align Text		Moves and rotates dimension text
LEADER		Dimension/Leader		Creates a leader line with attached annotation to a feature
QLEADER		Dimension/Leader	LE	Creates a leader and annotation
TOLERANCE		Dimension/ Tolerance	TOL	Creates geometric tolerances

Information Sharing

Command	Button	Menu option	Alias	Description
ADCCLOSE				Closes AutoCAD DesignCenter
ADCENTER		Tools/AutoCAD DesignCenter	ADC, CE	Manages and inserts content such as blocks, xrefs, and hatch patterns
ADCNAVIGATE				Controls the DesignCenter file name, folder, and network paths
BMPOUT				Saves selected objects to a file in device-independent bitmap format
BROWSER				Launches the default Web browser defined in your system's registry
COPYCLIP		Edit/Copy		Copies objects to the Clipboard
COPYLINK		Edit/Copy Link	CL	Copies the current view to the Clipboard for linking to other OLE applications
CUTCLIP		Edit/Cut		Copies objects to the Clipboard and erases the objects from the drawing

Command	Button	Menu option	Alias	Description
EXPORT		File/Export	EXP	Saves objects to other file formats
HYPERLINK		Insert/Hyperlink		Attaches a hyperlink to a graphical object or modifies an existing hyperlink
HYPERLINKOPTIONS				Controls the display of the hyperlink cursor and of the hyperlink tooltips
IMAGE			IM	Lists and modifies paths of images inserted into a drawing file
IMAGEFRAME		Modify/Object/ Image Frame		Controls whether image frames are displayed or hidden from view
IMPORT			IMP	Imports various file formats into AutoCAD LT
INSERT		Insert/Block	I	Inserts a block or another drawing
INSERTOBJ		Insert/OLE Object	IO	Inserts a linked or embedded object
MEETNOW		Tools/Meet Now		Shares an AutoCAD LT session among multiple users across a network
MSLIDE				Creates a slide file of the current viewport
OLELINKS		Edit/OLE Links		Updates, changes, and cancels existing links
OLESCALE				Controls the size, scale, and other properties of a selected OLE object
PASTECLIP		Edit/Paste	PC	Inserts data from the Clipboard
PASTESPEC		Edit/Paste Special	PA	Inserts data from the Clipboard and controls the format of the data

Command	Button	Menu option	Alias	Description
PUBLISHTOWEB		File/Publish to Web *or* Tools/Wizards/Publish to Web		Creates HTML pages that include images of selected AutoCAD LT drawings
SELECTURL				Selects all objects that have URLs attached
VSLIDE			VS	Displays a raster image slide file in the current viewport
WMFIN		Insert/ Windows MetaFile	WI	Imports a Windows metafile
WMFOPTS				Sets options for WMFIN
WMFOUT			WO	Saves objects to a file in Windows metafile format
XATTACH		Insert/ External Reference	XA	Attaches an external reference to the current drawing
XBIND		Modify/Object/External Reference Bind	XB	Binds dependent symbols of an xref to the current drawing
XREF		Insert/Xref Manager	XR	Controls external references to drawing files

Creating Layouts and Plotting

Command	Button	Menu option	Alias	Description
CONVERTCTB				Converts a color-dependent plot style table (CTB) to a named plot style table (STB)
CONVERTPSTYLES				Converts the current drawing to use named or color-dependent plot styles
LAYOUT		Insert/Layout/ New Layout		Creates and modifies drawing Layout tabs
LAYOUTWIZARD		Tools/Wizards/ Create Layout		Creates a new Layout tab and specifies page and plot settings
'LTSCALE		Format/Linetypes/ Detail	LTS	Sets the global linetype scale factor

Command	Button	Menu option	Alias	Description
MVIEW		View/Viewports/ 1, 2, 3, 4, Viewports	MV	Creates and controls layout viewports
PAGESETUP		File/Page Setup		Specifies the layout page, plotting device, paper size, and settings for each new layout
PLOT		File/Plot	PP	Plots a drawing to a plotting device or file
PLOTSTAMP				Places a plot stamp on a specified corner of each drawing and/or logs it to a file
PLOTSTYLE				Sets the current plot style for new objects or the assigned plot style for selected objects
PLOTTERMANAGER		File/Plotter Manager		Displays the Plotter Manager, where you can launch the Add-a-Plotter wizard and the Plotter Configuration Editor
PREVIEW		File/Plot Preview	PRE	Shows how the drawing will look when it is printed or plotted
PSETUPIN				Imports a user-defined page setup into a new drawing layout
SCALE		Modify/Scale	SC	Enlarges or reduces objects equally in the X, Y, and Z directions
STYLESMANAGER		File/Plot Style Manager		Displays the Plot Style Manager
VPLAYER			VL	Sets layer visibility within layout viewports
VPORTS		View/ Viewports		Creates multiple viewports

Command	Button	Menu option	Alias	Description

Command	Button	Menu option	Alias	Description

Task-Based Command Summary (*continued*)

Command	Button	Menu option	Alias	Description

Configuring a Digitizing Tablet

| REINIT | | | RI | Reinitializes the input/output ports, digitizer, display, and program parameters file |
| TABLET | | Tools/Tablet | TA | Calibrates and configures the tablet; turns Tablet mode on and off |

Managing and Repairing Drawing Files

AUDIT		File/Drawing Utilities/ Audit		Evaluates the integrity of a drawing
COPYHIST				Copies the text in the command line history window to the Clipboard
DWGPROPS		File/Drawing Properties		Sets and displays the file properties of the current drawing
LOGFILEOFF				Closes the log file opened by LOGFILEON
LOGFILEON				Writes the text window contents to a file
RECOVER		File/Drawing Utilities/ Recover		Repairs a damaged drawing
'TIME		Tools/Inquiry/ Time		Displays the date and time statistics of a drawing
WHOHAS				Displays ownership information for opened drawing files

Command	Button	Menu option	Alias	Description

Task-Based Command Summary (*continued*)

Command	Button	Menu option	Alias	Description
Working with Scripts				
DELAY				Provides a timed pause within a script
'RESUME				Continues an interrupted script
RSCRIPT				Repeats a script file
SCRIPT		Tools/Run Script	SCR	Executes a sequence of commands from a script

Glossary

Commands associated with definitions are shown in parentheses at the end of the definition.

absolute coordinates   Coordinate values measured from a coordinate system's origin point. *See also* **origin, relative coordinates, user coordinate system (UCS), world coordinates,** *and* **World Coordinate System (WCS).**

ADI   For *Autodesk Device Interface*. An interface specification for developing device drivers that are required for peripherals to work with AutoCAD LT and other Autodesk products.

affine transformation   A tablet calibration method that provides an arbitrary linear transformation in two-dimensional space. Affine transformation requires three calibration points to allow a tablet transformation that combines translation, independent X and Y scaling, rotation, and some skewing. Use affine transformation if a drawing has been stretched differently in the horizontal or vertical direction. (TABLET)

alias   A shortcut for an AutoCAD LT command. For example, *CP* is an alias for COPY, and *Z* is an alias for ZOOM. You define aliases in the *aclt.pgp* file.

aligned dimension   A dimension that measures the distance between two points at any angle. The dimension line is parallel to the line connecting the dimension's definition points. (DIMALIGNED)

angular dimension   A dimension that measures angles or arc segments and consists of text, extension lines, and dimension line arcs. (DIMANGULAR)

angular unit   The unit of measurement for an angle. Angular units can be measured in decimal degrees, degrees/minutes/seconds, grads, and radians. (UNITS)

annotations   Text, dimensions, tolerances, symbols, or notes.

anonymous block   An unnamed block that AutoCAD LT creates to support associative dimensions.

ANSI   For *American National Standards Institute*. Coordinator of voluntary standards development for both private and public sectors in the United States. Standards include programming languages, Electronic Data Interchange (EDI), telecommunications, and the physical properties of diskettes, cartridges, and magnetic tapes.

approximation points   Point locations that a B-spline must pass near, within a fit tolerance. *See also* **fit points** *and* **interpolation points**.

array   Multiple copies of selected AutoCAD LT objects in a rectangular or polar (radial) pattern. (ARRAY)

arrowhead   A terminator, such as an arrowhead, slash, or dot, at the end of a dimension line showing where a dimension begins and ends.

ASCII   For *American Standard Code for Information Interchange*. A common numeric code used in computer data communications. The code assigns meaning to 128 numbers, using seven bits per character with the eighth bit used for parity checking. Nonstandard versions of ASCII assign meaning to 255 numbers.

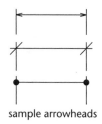
sample arrowheads

aspect ratio   Ratio of display width to height.

associative dimension   A dimension that adapts as the associated geometry is modified.

associative hatching   Hatching that conforms to its bounding objects such that modifying the bounding objects automatically adjusts the hatch. (BHATCH)

attribute definition   An AutoCAD LT object that is included in a block definition to store alphanumeric data. Attribute values can be predefined or specified when the block is inserted. Attribute data can be extracted from a drawing and inserted into external files. (ATTDEF)

attribute extraction file   An ASCII text file to which extracted attribute data is written. The contents and format are determined by the attribute extraction template file.

attribute extraction template file   An ASCII text file that determines which attributes are extracted and how they are formatted when written to an attribute extraction file.

attribute prompt   The text string displayed when you insert a block with an attribute whose value is undefined.

attribute tag   A text string associated with an attribute that identifies a particular attribute during extraction from the drawing database.

attribute value   The alphanumeric information associated with an **attribute tag**.

AutoCAD LT library search path   The order in which AutoCAD LT looks for a support file: current folder, drawing folder, folder specified in the support path, and folder containing the AutoCAD LT executable file, *aclt.exe*.

AutoSnap   The marker, tooltip, and magnetic action that can be used to identify an object snap.

baseline   An imaginary line on which text characters appear to rest. Individual characters can have descenders that drop below the baseline.

baseline dimension   Multiple dimensions measured from the same baseline. Also called *parallel dimension*. (DIMBASELINE)

base point   1. In the context of editing grips, the grip that changes to a solid color when selected to specify the focus of the subsequent editing operation. 2. A point for relative distance and angle when copying, moving, and rotating objects. 3. The insertion base point of the current drawing. (BASE) 4. The insertion base point for a block definition. (BLOCK)

Bezier curve   A polynomial curve defined by a set of control points, representing an equation of an order one less than the number of points being considered. A Bezier curve is a special case of a B-spline curve.

bitmap   The digital representation of an image having bits referenced to pixels. In color graphics, a different value represents each red, green, and blue component of a pixel.

blip marks   Temporary screen markers displayed in the AutoCAD LT graphics area when you specify a point or select objects. (BLIPMODE)

block   A generic term for one or more AutoCAD LT objects that are combined to create a single object. Commonly used for either block definition or block reference. *See* **block definition** *and* **block reference**. (BLOCK)

block definition   The name, base point, and set of objects that are combined and stored in the definition table of a drawing. (BLOCK) *See* **block**. *See also* **block reference**.

block library   *See* **symbol library**.

block reference   A compound object that is inserted in a drawing and displays the data stored in a block definition. Also called *instance*. *See* **block**. *See also* **block definition**. (INSERT)

block table   The nongraphic data area of a drawing file that stores block definitions. *See also* **definition table**.

Boolean operation   A mathematical method of expressing relationships using logical operators such as AND, OR, and NOT. With AutoCAD LT, Boolean operations can be performed with regions by using INTERSECT (AND), UNION (OR), and SUBTRACT (NOT).

B-spline curve   A blended piecewise polynomial curve passing near a given set of control points. (SPLINE)

button menu   The menu for a pointing device with multiple buttons. Each button on the pointing device (except the pick button) can be defined in the AutoCAD LT menu file *aclt.mnu* in the BUTTONS*n* and AUX*n* sections.

BYBLOCK   A special object property used to specify that the object inherits the color or linetype of any block containing it. *See also* **BYLAYER**.

BYLAYER   A special object property used to specify that the object inherits the color or linetype associated with its layer. *See also* **BYBLOCK**.

centroid   The center of mass of an object. In AutoCAD LT, use MASSPROP to find the centroid of a region or an AutoCAD-generated 3D solid.

circular external reference   An externally referenced drawing (xref) that references itself directly or indirectly. AutoCAD LT ignores the xref that creates the circular condition.

clipping planes   The boundaries that define or clip the field of view. (DVIEW)

CMYK   For *cyan, magenta, yellow, and key color*. A system of defining colors by specifying the percentages of cyan, magenta, yellow, and the key color, which is typically black.

color map   A table defining the intensity of red, green, and blue (RGB) for each displayed color.

command line   A text area reserved for keyboard input, prompts, and messages.

construction plane   A plane on which planar geometry is constructed. The *XY* plane of the current user coordinate system (UCS) represents the construction plane. *See also* **elevation** *and* **user coordinate system**.

continued dimension   A type of linear dimension that uses the second extension line origin of a selected dimension as its first extension line origin, breaking one long dimension into shorter segments that add up to the total measurement. Also called *chain dimension*. (DIMCONTINUE)

control frame   A series of point locations used as a mechanism to control the shape of a B-spline. These points are connected by a series of line segments for visual clarity and to distinguish the control frame from fit points. The SPLFRAME system variable must be turned on to display control frames.

control point   *See* **control frame**.

coordinate filters   Functions that extract individual *X*, *Y*, and *Z* coordinate values from different points to create a new, composite point. Also called *X,Y,Z point filters*.

crosshairs   A type of cursor consisting of two lines that intersect. Also called *graphics cursor*.

crosshairs

crossing polygon   A multisided area specified to select objects fully or partially within its borders. *See also* **crossing selection, window selection,** *and* **window polygon**.

crossing selection   A rectangular selection area drawn from right to left to select objects fully or partly within its borders. *See also* **crossing polygon, window polygon,** *and* **window selection**.

cursor   A pointer on a video display screen that can be moved around to place textual or graphical information. Also called *graphics cursor*. *See also* **crosshairs**.

cursor menu   *See* **object snap menu**.

default   A predefined value for a program input or parameter. Default values and options for AutoCAD LT commands are denoted by angle brackets < > and square brackets [ ] respectively.

default drawing   *See* **initial environment**.

definition points   Points created as part of an associative dimension. AutoCAD LT uses the points to modify the appearance and value of an associative dimension when the associated object is modified. Also called *defpoints* and stored on the special layer DEFPOINTS.

definition table   The data within an AutoCAD LT drawing file that stores the drawing's named objects. *See also* **named object.**

dependent objects   Named objects brought into a drawing by an external reference. *See also* **definition table** *and* **named object.**

DIESEL   For *Direct Interpretively Evaluated String Expression Language*. A macro language for altering the AutoCAD LT status line with the MODEMACRO system variable and for customizing menu items.

digitize   To convert a paper drawing or image into a computer file format by tracing it on an electronic tablet. This method is often used to enter map data. (TABLET)

dimension line arc   An arc (usually with arrows at each end) spanning the angle formed by the extension lines of an angle being measured. The dimension text near this arc sometimes divides it into two arcs. *See also* **angular dimension.**

dimension style   A named group of dimension settings that determines the appearance of the dimension and simplifies setting dimension system variables. (DIMSTYLE)

dimension text   The measurement value of dimensioned objects.

dimensioning system variables   A set of numeric values, text strings, and settings that control AutoCAD LT dimensioning features. (DIMSTYLE)

direct distance entry   A method of specifying a second point by first moving the cursor to indicate direction and then entering a distance.

dithering   Combining color dots to give the impression of displaying more colors than are actually available.

drawing extents   The smallest rectangle that contains all objects in a drawing, positioned on the screen to display the largest possible view of all objects. (ZOOM)

drawing limits   The user-defined rectangular boundary of the drawing area covered by dots when the grid is turned on. Also called *grid limits*. (LIMITS)

DWF   For *drawing Web format*. A highly compressed file format that is created from a DWG file. DWF files are easy to publish and view on the Internet. (PLOT)

DWG   Standard file format for saving vector graphics from within AutoCAD LT.

DXF   For *drawing interchange format*. An ASCII or binary file format of an AutoCAD LT drawing file for exporting AutoCAD LT drawings to other applications or for importing drawings from other applications. (SAVEAS, OPEN)

elevation   The default *Z* value above or below the *XY* plane of the current user coordinate system (UCS). Elevation is used for entering coordinates and digitizing locations. (ELEV)

embed   To use object linking and embedding (OLE) information from a source document in a destination document. An embedded object is a copy of the information from a source document that is placed in the destination document and has no link to the source document. *See also* **link.** (PASTESPEC)

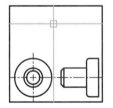

drawing extents

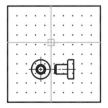

drawing limits

environment variable   A setting stored in the operating system that controls the operation of a program.

explode   To disassemble a complex object, such as a block or polyline, into simpler objects. In the case of a block, the block definition is unchanged. The block reference is replaced by the components of the block. *See also* **block, block definition,** *and* **block reference.** (EXPLODE)

extents   *See* **drawing extents.**

external reference (xref)   A drawing file referenced by another drawing. (XREF)

fence   A multisegmented line specified to select objects it passes through.

fill   A solid color covering an area bounded by lines or curves. (FILL)

fit points   Locations that a B-spline must pass through exactly or within a fit tolerance. *See also* **interpolation points** *and* **approximation points.**

fit tolerance   The setting for the maximum distance that a B-spline can pass for each of the fit points that define it.

floating viewports   *See* **layout viewports.**

font   A character set, comprising letters, numbers, punctuation marks, and symbols, of a distinctive proportion and design.

freeze   A setting that suppresses the display of objects on selected layers. Objects on frozen layers are not displayed, regenerated, or plotted. Freezing layers shortens regenerating time. *See also* **thaw.** (LAYER)

graphics area   The area of the AutoCAD LT screen for creating and editing a drawing.

graphics cursor   *See* **crosshairs** *and* **cursor.**

graphics screen   *See* **graphics window.**

graphics window   The graphics area, its surrounding menus, and the command line.

grid   An area in the graphics area covered with regularly spaced dots to aid drawing. The spacing between grid dots is adjustable. Grid dots are not plotted. *See also* **drawing limits.** (GRID)

grip modes   The editing capabilities activated when grips are displayed on an object: stretching, moving, rotating, scaling, and mirroring.

grips   Small squares that appear on objects you select. After selecting the grip, you edit the object by dragging it with the pointing device in combination with grip modes and options.

group   A collection of AutoCAD LT objects that are associated into a set for convenient editing. Groups can be assigned a name and a description. (GROUP)

HDI driver   For *Heidi Device Interface*. An interface for developing device drivers that are required for peripherals to work with AutoCAD LT and other Autodesk products.

home page   The main navigating screen for a Web site.

IGES   For *initial graphics exchange specification*. An ANSI-standard format for digital representation and exchange of information between CAD/CAM systems.

included angle   The interior angle that defines the endpoints of an arc or the extents of a polar array in AutoCAD LT.

initial environment   The variables and settings for new drawings as defined by the default template drawing, such as *aclt.dwt* or *acltiso.dwt*. *See also* **template drawing**.

IntelliMouse   *See* **wheel mouse**.

interpolation points   Defining points that a B-spline passes through. *See also* **approximation points** *and* **fit points**.

island   An enclosed area within a hatched area.

ISO   For *International Standards Organization*. The organization that sets international standards in all fields except electrical and electronics. Headquarters are in Geneva, Switzerland.

isometric snap style   An AutoCAD LT drafting option that aligns the cursor with two of three isometric axes and displays grid points, making isometric drawings easier to create. (DSETTINGS)

justification   In AutoCAD LT, the alignment of paragraph text, single-line text, leader text, and text with dimensions.

layer   A logical grouping of data similar to transparent acetate overlays on a drawing. You can view and plot layers individually or in combination. (LAYER)

layout   The arrangement of views in a drawing.

layout viewports   Rectangular objects that display views on a Layout tab in paper space. *See also* **paper space**. **(MVIEW, VPORTS)**

limits   *See* **drawing limits**.

line font   *See* **linetype**.

line width   *See* **lineweight**.

linetype   How a line or type of curve is displayed. For example, a continuous line has a different linetype than a dashed line. Also called *line font*. (LINETYPE)

lineweight   A width value that can be assigned to all graphical objects except TrueType fonts and raster images. In AutoCAD LT, line width can be controlled by specifying the lineweight property, specifying a plot style for plotting, or specifying a width for polylines. Lineweight should not be confused with thickness, which gives an appearance of three-dimensional depth to objects. (LWEIGHT, PLOT)

link   To use object linking and embedding (OLE) to reference data in another file. When data is linked, any changes to it in the source document are automatically updated in any destination document. *See also* **embed**. (COPYLINK)

markup file   *See* **RML**.

markups   The annotations that are added to drawings using Autodesk Volo View. Markups can be textual comments, sketched or drawn changes, or measurements. Also called *redlines*. *See also* **RML**.

mass properties   Computed values of 2D regions and AutoCAD-generated 3D solids. In AutoCAD LT, mass properties include area, perimeter, centroid, and moments of inertia. (MASSPROP)

mirror   To create a new version of an existing object by reflecting it symmetrically with respect to a prescribed line or plane. (MIRROR)

model   A two- or three-dimensional representation of an object.

model space   One of the two primary spaces in which AutoCAD LT objects reside. Typically, a geometric model is placed in a three-dimensional coordinate space called model space. A final layout of specific views and annotations of this model is placed in paper space. *See also* **paper space**. (MSPACE)

named object   A term that describes the various types of nongraphical information, such as styles and definitions, stored with an AutoCAD LT drawing. Named objects include blocks, dimension styles, layers, layouts, linetypes, text styles, views, and viewport configurations. Named objects are stored in definition tables.

named view   A view saved for restoration later. (VIEW)

node   An object snap specification to locate points, dimension definition points, and dimension text origins.

noun-verb selection   Selecting an object first and then using a command on it rather than starting a command first and then selecting the object.

NURBS   For *nonuniform rational B-spline curve*. A B-spline curve or surface defined by a series of weighted control points and one or more knot vectors. *See* **B-spline curve**.

object   One or more AutoCAD LT graphical elements, such as text, dimensions, lines, circles, or polylines, treated as a single element for creation, manipulation, and modification. Also called *entity*.

object properties   Settings that control the appearance and geometric characteristics of AutoCAD LT objects. Properties that are common to all objects include color, layer, linetype, linetype scale, and 3D thickness. (PROPERTIES)

object snap menu   The menu that is displayed in the graphics area at the cursor location when you hold down SHIFT and right-click the pointing device. Also called a cursor menu, it is defined in the POP0 section of *aclt.mnu*. *See also* **shortcut menu**.

object snap override   Turning off or changing a running object snap setting for input of a single point. *See also* **object snaps** *and* **running object snap**.

object snaps   Methods for selecting commonly needed points on an object while you create or edit an AutoCAD LT drawing. *See also* **running object snap** *and* **object snap override**. (OSNAP)

OLE   For *object linking and embedding*. An information-sharing method in which data from a source document can be linked to or embedded in a destination document. Selecting the data in the destination document opens the source application so that the data can be edited. *See also* **embed** *and* **link**.

origin   The point where coordinate axes intersect. For example, the origin of a Cartesian coordinate system is where the X, Y, and Z axes meet at 0,0,0.

Ortho   An AutoCAD LT setting that limits pointing device input to horizontal or vertical (relative to the current snap angle and the user coordinate system). *See also* **snap angle** *and* **user coordinate system**. (ORTHO)

orthogonal calibration A tablet calibration method that provides a transformation in two-dimensional space with uniform scaling and rotation. Orthogonal calibration requires two calibration points to allow a tablet transformation that combines translation and rotation only. (TABLET)

pan To shift the view of a drawing without changing magnification. *See also* **zoom**. (PAN)

paper space One of two primary spaces in which AutoCAD LT objects reside. Paper space is used for creating a finished layout for printing or plotting, as opposed to doing drafting or design work. Model space is used for creating the drawing. *See also* **model space**, **viewport**. (PSPACE)

PC2 file Complete plotter configuration file. PC2 files contain all plot settings and device-specific settings that were saved in previous versions of AutoCAD LT. *See also* **PCP file** *and* **PC3 file**.

PC3 file Partial plotter configuration file. PC3 files contain plot settings information such as the device driver and model, the output port to which the device is connected, and various device-specific settings, but they do not include any custom plotter calibration or custom paper size information. *See also* **PC2 file** *and* **PCP file**.

PCP file Partial plotter configuration file. PCP files contain basic plot specifications and pen parameters that were saved in previous versions of AutoCAD LT. Plot settings that are stored in a PCP file include pen assignments, plotting units, paper size, plot rotation, plot origin, scale factor, and pen optimization level. *See also* **PC2 file** *and* **PC3 file**.

pick button The button on a pointing device that is used to select objects or specify points on the screen. For example, on a mouse, it is the left button.

plan view

plan view A view orientation from a point on the positive Z axis toward the origin (0,0,0). (PLAN)

pline *See* **polyline**.

point 1. A location in three-dimensional space specified by *X*, *Y*, and *Z* coordinate values. 2. An AutoCAD LT object consisting of a single coordinate location. (POINT)

pointing device A device, such as a mouse or a digitizing puck, that can be used to interact with AutoCAD LT's interface and create and edit drawing objects in the graphics area. A pointing device usually has several buttons, some of which may be customized to perform commands you specify.

polar array Objects copied around a specified center point a specified number of times. (ARRAY)

polar snap A drawing aid for constraining the cursor to increments of a specified distance along a polar tracking angle. *See also* **snap grid**.

polar tracking A way to locate a point that provides visual guidelines corresponding to increments of a specified angle. (POLAR)

polyline An AutoCAD LT object composed of one or more connected line segments or circular arcs treated as a single object. Also called *pline*. (PLINE, PEDIT)

projective calibration   A tablet calibration method, also called *rubber sheeting* by cartographers, that provides a transformation equivalent to perspective projection of any plane in space onto another plane. Projective calibration requires four calibration points to allow a tablet transformation that accommodates a certain degree of stretching in the original paper drawing. Projective transformation corrects parallel lines that appear to converge. (TABLET)

prompt   A message on the command line that asks for information or requests action such as specifying a point.

properties   *See* **object properties**.

purge   An AutoCAD LT feature that removes unused definitions such as block definitions, layers, and text styles from a drawing. (PURGE)

redraw   To quickly refresh or clean up blip marks in the current viewport without updating the drawing's database. *See also* **regenerate**. (REDRAW)

regenerate   To update a drawing's screen display by recomputing the screen coordinates from the database. *See also* **redraw**. (REGEN)

regions   A type of object in AutoCAD LT that encloses an area and can be combined with other regions using Boolean operations. AutoCAD LT can also compute the mass properties of regions. (REGION, UNION, SUBTRACT, INTERSECT, MASSPROP)

relative coordinates   Coordinates specified in relation to previous coordinates.

RGB   For *red, green, and blue*. A system of defining colors by specifying percentages of red, green, and blue.

RML   For *redline markup language*. A file format that is used for saving markups in Autodesk Volo View. RML files can be inserted into drawing files using AutoCAD LT. (RMLIN)

rubber-band line   A line that stretches dynamically on the screen with the movement of the cursor. One endpoint of the line is attached to a point in your drawing, and the other is attached to the moving cursor.

running object snap   An object snap set so it continues for subsequent selections. (OSNAP) *See also* **object snap** *and* **object snap override**.

scale   1. The proportional size of an object compared with other objects. 2. The display size of the components of noncontinuous linetypes and hatches. 3. The apparent size of objects in a view with respect to a drawing sheet. (SCALE, HPSCALE, LTSCALE, CELTSCALE, ZOOM)

script file   A set of AutoCAD LT commands executed sequentially with a single SCRIPT command. Script files are created outside AutoCAD LT using a text editor, saved in text format, and stored in an external file with the extension *.scr*.

selection set   One or more AutoCAD LT objects specified for processing as a unit. (OPTIONS)

selection window   *See* **window selection**.

shortcut menu   The menu that is displayed in the command window, text window, or graphics area at the cursor location when you right-click the pointing device. The shortcut menu commands vary depending upon the screen context and whether an object is selected. The shortcut menu provides easy access to editing commands when editing with grips. *See also* **object snap menu.**

slide file A file that contains a raster image or snapshot of the objects displayed in the graphics area. Slide files have the file extension *.sld.* (MSLIDE, VSLIDE)

slide library A collection of slide files organized for convenient retrieval and display. Slide library names have the extension.*slb* and are created with the *slidelib.exe* utility.

snap *See* **snap angle, snap grid, snap resolution,** *and* **polar snap.**

snap angle The angle at which the snap grid is rotated. (SNAP)

snap grid The invisible grid that locks the graphics cursor into alignment with the grid points according to the spacing set by SNAP. Snap grid does not necessarily correspond to the visible grid, which is controlled separately by GRID. (SNAP)

snap resolution The spacing between points of the snap grid. (SNAP)

spline *See* **B-spline curve** *and* **NURBS.**

strings A sequence of text characters entered at a prompt or in a dialog box.

symbol library A collection of block definitions stored in a single AutoCAD LT drawing file.

symbol table *See* **definition table.**

symbols In AutoCAD LT, a collection of objects saved as a single object known as a *block. See also* **block, block definition,** and **block reference.** (BLOCK INSERT, ADCENTER)

system variable A name that AutoCAD LT recognizes as a setting, size, or limit. Read-only system variables, such as DWGNAME, cannot be modified directly by the user.

template drawing A drawing file with preestablished settings for new drawings, such as *aclt.dwt* and *acltiso.dwt*; however, any drawing can be saved and used as a template. *See also* **initial environment.**

temporary files Data files created during an AutoCAD LT session. AutoCAD LT deletes the files by the time you end the session. If the session ends abnormally, such as during a power outage, temporary files might be left on the disk.

text style A named, saved collection of settings that determines the appearance of text characters—for example, stretched, compressed, oblique, mirrored, or set in a vertical column. (STYLE)

thaw A setting that displays previously frozen layers. *See also* **freeze.** (LAYER)

thickness The distance certain objects are extruded to give them a 3D appearance. (CHPROP, PROPERTIES, ELEV, THICKNESS)

tiled viewports A type of display that splits the AutoCAD LT graphics area into one or more adjacent rectangular viewing areas. *See also* **layout viewports, TILEMODE,** *and* **viewport.** (VPORTS)

toolbar Part of the AutoCAD LT interface containing buttons that represent commands.

tracking A way to locate a point relative to other points on the drawing. *See also* **polar tracking.** (TRACKING)

transparent command   A command started while another is in progress. Precede transparent commands with an apostrophe.

tree view   A hierarchical list that can be expanded or collapsed to control the amount of information displayed. In AutoCAD LT, tree views are available in AutoCAD DesignCenter, the Purge dialog box, the External Reference dialog box, and the online Help system.

UCS   *See* **user coordinate system.**

UCS icon   An icon that indicates the orientation of the UCS axes. (UCSICON)

UCS icon

user coordinate system (UCS)   A user-defined coordinate system that defines the origin and orientation of the *X*, *Y*, and *Z* axes in 3D space. The UCS determines the default placement of geometry in a drawing. *See also* **World Coordinate System.** (UCS)

vector   A mathematical entity with precise direction and length but without specific location.

vertex   A location where edges or polyline segments meet.

view   A graphical representation of a model from a specific location (viewpoint) in space. *See also* **viewpoint** *and* **viewport.** (VPOINT, DVIEW, VIEW)

viewpoint   The location in 3D model space from which you are viewing a model. *See also* **view** *and* **viewport.** (DVIEW, VPOINT)

viewport   A bounded area that displays some portion of the model space of a drawing. On a Layout tab, viewports are objects that can be moved and resized. On the Model tab, viewports are noneditable, nonoverlapping screen displays. *See also* **layout viewport.**

viewport configuration   A named collection of model space viewports that can be saved and restored. (VPORTS)

WCS   *See* **World Coordinate System.**

wheel mouse   A two-button mouse with a small wheel between the buttons. You can zoom and pan your drawing using the wheel, without using any commands from AutoCAD LT. Clicking the wheel is equivalent to clicking the middle button on a three-button mouse.

window polygon   A multisided polygon area specified to select objects contained completely within its borders. *See also* **crossing polygon, crossing selection,** *and* **window selection.**

window selection   A rectangular selection area drawn from left to right in the AutoCAD LT graphics area to select objects contained completely within its borders. *See also* **crossing polygon, crossing selection,** *and* **window polygon.**

working drawing   A drawing for manufacturing or building purposes, displayed in the graphics area.

WCS icon

wireframe model   The representation of an object using lines and curves to represent its boundaries.

world coordinates   Coordinates expressed in relation to the World Coordinate System.

World Coordinate System (WCS)   A coordinate system used as the basis for defining all objects and other coordinate systems.

xref   *See* **external reference.**

X,Y,Z **point filters**   *See* **coordinate filters.**

zoom   To reduce or increase the apparent magnification of the graphics display. (ZOOM)

Index

We'd like to take credit for designing the world's finest software, but the truth is that much of the credit goes to you, our customer. If you have an idea for a new feature in the next release of one of our products, or hope to see an existing feature improved, please let us know.

AUTODESK   WISHLIST

Address Information

Please send to:
Autodesk, Inc.
111 McInnis Parkway
San Rafael, CA 94903
Attn: Wish List
You can also submit wishlist items through the Autodesk Web page at
www.autodesk.com/wishlist

Name

Company

Date

Address

Phone number

City

Extension

State   ZIP/Postal Code

Email address

Country

Complete this section only if you are an Authorized Dealer:

Your customer's name

Your customer's phone number

Please identify the Autodesk product this request is for:

Please indicate the product release (or version) you are currently using:

Product   Serial Number   Platform/Operating System

Choose the category that best fits your request:

☐ New Feature or Command   ☐ Printer/Plotter Support

☐ Feature or Command Enhancement   ☐ Platform Support

☐ Documentation Change   ☐ Installation and Configuration

☐ Display Support   ☐ Customization

☐ Digitizer Support   ☐ General

☐ Operating System Support   ☐ Other_____

If applicable, indicate which feature or command this request relates to:

continued on back

Describe your request in detail below (one request per sheet):

_____

_____

_____

_____

_____

_____

_____

_____

_____

_____

_____

Please indicate the reasons for your request (i.e., what would be the benefits of your request and what problems would it solve?):

_____

_____

_____

_____

Thank You   We appreciate your interest in our products, and will consider your suggestions in our future product development.

Despite rigorous product testing, some problems simply cannot be detected in advance. Let us know if you discover what may be a bug in our software. We'll address the problem, so that our software can take care of your business.

AUTODESK — BUG REPORT

Instructions

1. Please fill in the form **completely**. Fill in the release number and serial number for your Autodesk product (AutoCAD®, Mechanical Desktop®, etc.). Be sure to provide **ALL** the information about your system, as these specifics are important. For peripherals, specify actual make and model. If the peripheral is emulating another make or model, please note what that is. Please indicate all network information requested on this form.

2. Under **Problem Description**, describe the problem clearly and completely. We want to be able to re-create your problem, so we need to know the exact sequence of activities that led up to it. Include the exact error message, if one appeared. Use a separate sheet of paper if necessary. Please include information about programs, services, or utilities that are running but not a part of the native operating system.

3. If your problem concerns a particular drawing, please enclose a drawing disk. Attach any other relevant materials and check the corresponding boxes.

4. Mail to:

   Autodesk, Inc.
   111 McInnis Parkway
   San Rafael, CA 94903
   Attn: Bug Report

Address Information

Name	Company
Date	Address
Phone number	
Extension ZIP/Postal Code	City State
Email address	Country

Complete this section only if you are an Authorized Dealer:

Your customer's name	Your customer's phone number

continued on back

Hardware and Software Information

Product Name

Serial Number

Computer Brand Name

Model

Operating System(s)/Version

Network Software/Version

Number of Nodes

Memory (Total RAM)

Hard Disk Space

Graphics Card(s)

Digitizer/Mouse

Plotter

☐ Serial   ☐ Parallel

Printer

☐ Serial   ☐ Parallel

Problem Description

Use this space to describe the problem. Be specific in the sequence of steps that led up to the problem and describe the exact results. Be sure to enclose copies of relevant materials: drawing files (on disk), script files, plots, etc.

Materials Enclosed

☐ Disk   ☐ Script   ☐ Letter   ☐ Print/Plot/Image

Imagine your artwork on the cover of an international magazine. Your drawing could be featured on the box of the next AutoCAD® or your animation could be included in the next Autodesk 3D Studio® Siggraph tape. Send us the best work that you have done using Autodesk® software, and we will do our best to get your images into the public eye!

AUTODESK | SEND US YOUR BEST WORK

It's Simple

1. Select your best work.

2. Complete and sign the Autodesk Archive Consent and Release Authorization form below.

3. Send your images and completed form to:

Autodesk, Inc.
111 McInnis Parkway
San Rafael, CA 94903
Attn: Marketing Support Team – Image Archives

Archive Consent and Release Authorization

We appreciate your interest in submitting material to Autodesk, Inc. The following allows us to legally use your work.

By signing and returning this consent form, I understand that I am agreeing to the following terms which will govern use of the images and other material (the "Material") described below:

I am granting a nonexclusive, irrevocable, perpetual, worldwide license to Autodesk, Inc., to use the images, and other material contained in the files described below (the "Material") in any manner it deems appropriate. Nonexclusive means that I can allow others to use the Material if I wish and that I retain all rights to the Material other than those specifically granted to Autodesk.

Autodesk may change, reproduce, distribute, and sublicense the Material to its customers and third parties permitting them the same rights Autodesk is entitled to grant.

Autodesk will try to include the credit line shown below when the Material is used and will also try to require others to whom it grants sublicense to do the same. Autodesk and its sublicensees may not always be able to include the credit line or otherwise acknowledge the source of the Material. I understand that the compensation I will receive for my agreement to license the Material will be limited to the exposure it receives by Autodesk's use and sublicensing of it and that no other compensation will be paid. I agree that I will not at any time make any claim for compensation for the rights I am granting to Autodesk.

I am over 18 years old and own the copyright to the material in these files, or have the right to grant this consent on behalf of the owner, or know that the material in these files is in the public domain. This consent does not conflict with any others I have granted or any other rights to the files.

Company Name (please print) | Name (please print)

Address | Signature

| Date

City | State | Telephone Number

ZIP/Postal Code | Country | FAX Number

continued on back

Submission Guidelines

Send us your images on DOS disks, CD-ROM, IOMEGA zip cartridge, or BETACAM SP tape[1]. Use PKZIP version 2.04 or greater to compress your data if necessary. Also, include a hard copy of each image if you can.

Be sure to include the original geometry with your submission. Also, remember to include all associated custom files (i.e. texture maps, patterns, linetypes, fonts, menus, etc.) as well.

If you have included proprietary information, logos, or trademarks in your image or animation, please send along written permission for their use from the owner(s).

The above release shall be void if amended in any manner. Autodesk shall not be responsible for the return of any files submitted.

Remember to clearly label each submission with the name of your file(s), your name, your company name, your daytime phone number, and fax number.

Please note that submitted media cannot be returned.

[1] Submitted videos should be BETACAM SP in NTSC format. However, we can also work with 3/4-inch SVHS, Hi-8, or VHS tape in PAL or SECAM formats. It is helpful when submitting an animation to include a representative frame rendered at 1024 x 768 (or higher) and in true color (24 or 32 bit color).

Please provide and initial a DOS listing if you have more than four files that you are submitting to Autodesk, Inc.

File name(s)*	Description	Software used	File size, date, time
Example: *capecod.tga*	Cape Cod vacation home	AutoCAD, 3D Studio	

*File names should be a maximum of eight characters, plus a maximum three-character extension.

❏ Check here if you have attached a printout for additional files. Please describe each file as shown in the example above.

Please indicate below what software was primarily used in the creation of the submitted image(s).

Although image credits cannot be guaranteed, if they can be granted how would you like them to appear?

NOTE: Sending in your art does not disqualify it from any consideration in any contest or offer we may hold in the future. You need only resubmit it at that time. All submissions become the property of Autodesk, Inc. Please retain duplicates of your submissions.